LECTURES ON CALCULUS

THE MATHESIS SERIES

KENNETH O. MAY, *Editor*

Lectures on Calculus

A. H. Copeland, Sr., M. K. Fort, Jr.,
H. W. Guggenheimer, J. D. Mancill,
M. E. Munroe, D. E. Richmond, H. Sagan,
A. Wilansky, O. Wyler

Edited by

KENNETH O. MAY

University of Toronto

HOLDEN-DAY

San Francisco, Cambridge, London, Amsterdam

Foreword

Since 1954 the Mathematical Association of America with support from the National Science Foundation has administered a program of visiting lecturers with the following general aims: (a) to strengthen and stimulate the mathematics programs of colleges; (b) to provide the mathematics staff and students in small colleges with an opportunity for personal contacts with productive and creative mathematicians; (c) to aid in the motivation of able college students to consider careers in mathematics and the teaching of mathematics; and (d) to create and strengthen ties between undergraduate colleges and graduate schools. The program has reached hundreds of colleges and thousands of undergraduate students, but universities offering the Doctor's degree in mathematics are not included, and many of the others have never had a visiting lecturer. In the belief that some of the values of these lectures could be transmitted in printed form and that both students and teachers of mathematics would welcome stimulating expositions by active mathematicians, we invited those who had participated in the program to prepare their favorite lectures for publication. This volume is the first result, and we hope it will be followed by other collections of live mathematics suitable for supplementary reading by students.

In spite of the current emphasis on algebra, topology, and other relatively new areas of mathematics, classical analysis—the structure developing most obviously from calculus—remains at the center of mathematical education and practice. Unfortunately it also remains one of the least exciting courses taken by the under-

v

graduate student, perhaps because the great ideas are obscured by routine manipulations and obsolete applications that have been incorporated in the courses over the years. Yet even the elementary course in calculus opens the doors to many treasure-houses of interesting ideas. The nine lectures printed here can be no more than a small sample, but we hope that they are representative. They include new approaches to familiar material, novel applications, and interesting introductions to modern developments. The lectures are arranged roughly in order of the knowledge and maturity required of the reader. Each is preceded by a bibliographical note on the author and indications of the paper's content and level.

K. O. M.

Toronto, Ontario
1967

Contents

1

Formal Logic as a Tool

for Mathematics

ARTHUR H. COPELAND, SR.

UNIVERSITY OF MICHIGAN

Arthur H. Copeland, Sr., Professor of Mathematics at the University of Michigan, is a native of New York. He graduated from Amherst College in 1921 and completed his Ph.D. at Harvard in 1926. Before coming to the University of Michigan he taught at Harvard, Rice Institute, and the University of Buffalo. He has been a Guggenheim Fellow and director of a project for the Office of Naval Research. His special interests are the foundations of probability, analysis, mechanics, and logic. He is author of *Geometry, Algebra and Trigonometry with the Aid of Vectors*.

In the following lecture Professor Copeland presents the simplest ideas of logic and illustrates their usefulness for understanding the concepts of continuity and uniform continuity.

FORMAL LOGIC AS A TOOL
FOR MATHEMATICS

Arthur H. Copeland, Sr.

Certain difficulties students have in mathematics are especially apparent in advanced calculus. When one analyzes some of the reasoning in this subject by means of formal logic it is discovered that this reasoning does have a peculiarity. Consider an example. A function f defined on an open interval containing a point x_0 is said to be continuous at x_0 if *for every* positive ε *there exists* a positive δ such that *for every* x we have

$$|f(x) - f(x_0)| < \varepsilon \text{ whenever } |x - x_0| < \delta.$$

The expressions "for every" and "there exists" are called *logical quantifiers*. Thus the definition of continuity is stated in terms of three quantifiers. The definition of uniform continuity requires four quantifiers, i.e., quadruple quantification. In ordinary conversation one encounters single quantification and on rare occasions double, but never triple or quadruple. To state what it means for a function to be discontinuous requires the formation of the negation of a sentence involving triple quantification. Many people are uncertain about the negation of a sentence involving a single quantification.

This suggests that some training in logic would be helpful in the study of advanced calculus. A small amount of logic is sufficient

3

and the logic is so closely related to the set theory usually presented in advanced calculus that the two subjects tend to reinforce one another. It is convenient to present both set theory and logic as studies in Boolean algebra. Thus the student can learn three subjects with little more effort than is required to learn one of them. The purpose of this paper is to indicate how these subjects can be so presented.

Let us start with the set theory. The points of a plane constitute a set of points called Euclidean 2-space and denoted by E^2. The points in three-dimensional space constitute a set denoted by E^3. If A and B are sets, the set consisting of all points that belong both to A and to B is called the *intersection* of A and B and is denoted by $A \cap B$. If A and B have no points in common, their intersection is called the *empty set* or *null set* and is denoted by $\varnothing$. The set consisting of the points that belong to A or to B or to both is called the *union* of A and B and is denoted by $A \cup B$. We shall consider a collection of sets (i.e., set of sets) denoted by $\mathscr{B}$. Each set of $\mathscr{B}$ is made up of points that belong to some space E. If A is a set of $\mathscr{B}$, then the points of E that do not belong to A constitute a set called the *complement* of A and are denoted by $\sim A$. Figure 1-1 shows an intersection, a union and a complement and indicates that $A \cap B = B \cap A$ and $A \cup B = B \cup A$. Figure 1-2

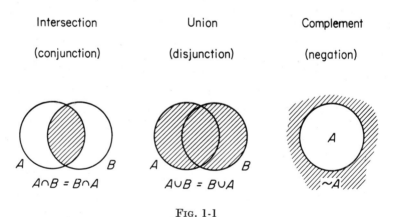

Intersection   Union   Complement

(conjunction)   (disjunction)   (negation)

$A \cap B = B \cap A$ $A \cup B = B \cup A$ $\sim A$

Fig. 1-1

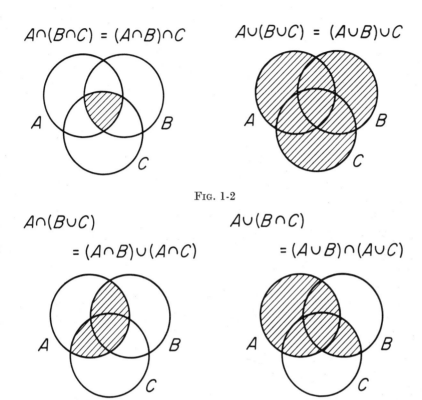

$$A \cap (B \cap C) = (A \cap B) \cap C \qquad A \cup (B \cup C) = (A \cup B) \cup C$$

Fig. 1-2

$$A \cap (B \cup C)$$
$$= (A \cap B) \cup (A \cap C) \qquad$$

$$A \cup (B \cap C)$$
$$= (A \cup B) \cap (A \cup C)$$

Fig. 1-3

indicates that $A \cap (B \cap C) = (A \cap B) \cap C$ and $A \cup (B \cup C) = (A \cup B) \cup C$. Figure 1-3 indicates that $A \cap (B \cup C) = (A \cap B) \cup (A \cap C)$ and $A \cup (B \cap C) = (A \cup B) \cap (A \cup C)$. These properties of the collection $\mathscr{B}$ and the operations $\cap$, $\cup$, $\sim$ are listed in the following postulates. These properties were first studied by George Boole and a collection having these properties is now called a *Boolean algebra*.

Postulate 1.   *If A and B are sets of $\mathscr{B}$, then $A \cap B$ and $A \cup B$ are sets of $\mathscr{B}$.*

Postulate 2. $A \cap B = B \cap A$ and $A \cup B = B \cup A$.

Postulate 3. $A \cap (B \cap C) = (A \cap B) \cap C$ *and* $A \cup (B \cup C) = (A \cup B) \cup C$.

Postulate 4. $A \cap (B \cup C) = (A \cap B) \cup (A \cap C)$ *and* $A \cup (B \cap C) = (A \cup B) \cap (A \cup C)$.

Postulate 5. $\mathscr{B}$ *contains a set* $\varnothing$ *such that* $A \cap \varnothing = \varnothing$ *and* $A \cup \varnothing = A$ *for every set* A *of* $\mathscr{B}$.

Postulate 6. $\mathscr{B}$ *contains a set* E *such that* $A \cup E = E$ *and* $A \cap E = A$ *for every set* A *of* $\mathscr{B}$.

Postulate 7.   *For every set* A *of* $\mathscr{B}$ *there exists a set* $\sim A$ *of* $\mathscr{B}$ *such that* $A \cap \sim A = \varnothing$ *and* $A \cup \sim A = E$.

On the basis of these postulates we can prove the following theorems.

Theorem 1.   *In any Boolean algebra the sets* $\varnothing$ *and* E *are unique.*

Theorem 2.   *If* A *and* B *are such that* $A \cap B = \varnothing$ *and* $A \cup B = E$, *then* $B = \sim A$.

Theorem 3. A *is unique and* $\sim (\sim A) = A$.

Theorem 4. $\sim (A \cap B) = (\sim A) \cup (\sim B)$ *and* $\sim (A \cup B) = (\sim A) \cap (\sim B)$ (*De Morgan's theorem*).

Theorem 5. $A \cap A = A = A \cup A$.

Theorem 6. $A \cap (A \cup B) = A = A \cup (A \cap B)$.

We introduce the following notation:

$$A_1 \cap A_2 \cap \cdots A_n = \bigcap_{k=1}^{n} A_k,$$

$$A_1 \cup A_2 \cup \cdots A_n = \bigcup_{k=1}^{n} A_k.$$

The intersection $A_1 \cap A_2 \cap \cdots A_n$ consists of the points common to the sets $A_1, \ldots, A_n$, i.e., a point belongs to this set if and only if *for every* k (where $k = 1, \ldots, n$) the point belongs to A_k. The union $A_1 \cup A_2 \cup \cdots A_n$ consists of the points that belong to at least one of the sets A_k, i.e., a point belongs to this set if and only if *there exists* k (where $k = 1, \ldots, n$) such that the point belongs to A_k. Note the quantifiers "for every" and "there exists." The following generalization of De Morgan's theorem is easily proved by mathematical induction.

Theorem 7. $\quad \sim \bigcap_{k=1}^{n} A_k = \bigcup_{k=1}^{n} \sim A_k \quad and \quad \sim \bigcup_{k=1}^{n} A_k = \bigcap_{k=1}^{n} \sim A_k.$

Let us see how set theory is related to logic. John Venn observed that it is instructive to picture sentences as regions in the plane. Regions are, of course, sets of points. If A and B are sentences each of which is pictured as a region, then the sentence "A and B" is called the *conjunction* of the two sentences and is pictured as the intersection of the two regions. It is thus appropriate to use the symbol $A \cap B$ to denote the conjunction "A and B." The sentence "A or B or both" is called the *disjunction* of the two sentences and is pictured as the union of the two regions. It is denoted by $A \cup B$. Unfortunately, the word "or" is ambiguous, i.e., the sentence "A or B" is sometimes interpreted as "A or B or both" and sometimes as "A or B but not both." We shall always use the former interpretation and it will be understood that "A or B" is an abbreviation for the disjunction "A or B or both." The sentence "*not A*" is called the *negation* of the sentence A. It is pictured as the complement of the region representing A and is denoted by $\sim A$. Thus Figure 1-1 can be interpreted as picturing a conjunction, a disjunction, and a negation. Such pictures are called *Venn diagrams*.

For any sentence A the sentence $A \cap \sim A$ is a *contradiction*. All contradictions are regarded as the same sentence and this sentence is denoted by the symbol for the null set, i.e., by $\varnothing$. The trivially true sentence $A \cup \sim A$ is called a *tautology*. All tautologies are regarded as the same sentence. This sentence is pictured as the whole space and is denoted by E. With these interpretations it is possible to regard the elements of a Boolean algebra as sentences.

If $A_1, \ldots, A_n$ are sentences, then the sentence "for every x, A_x (where $x = 1, \ldots, n$)" and the sentence "there exists x such that A_x (where $x = 1, \ldots, n$)" are denoted respectively by

$$A_1 \cap A_2 \cap \cdots A_n = \bigcap_{x=1}^{n} A_x \quad \text{and} \quad A_1 \cup \cdots A_n = \bigcup_{x=1}^{n} A_x.$$

Let A_x be a sentence about an element of some set S and let the symbol $x \in S$ indicate that x is an element of S. Then the sentence "for every x, A_x (where x is in the set S)" and the sentence "there exists x such that A_x (where x is in S)" are denoted respectively by

$$\bigcap_{x \in S} A_x \quad \text{and} \quad \bigcup_{x \in S} A_x.$$

For example, if C denotes the set of all real numbers, then the sentence "for every real number x we have $x + 0 = x$" is denoted by

$$\bigcap_{x \in C} (x + 0 = x).$$

When the range of x is understood, the sentences "for every x, A_x" and "there exists x such that A_x" are denoted by

$$\bigcap_x A_x \quad \text{and} \quad \bigcup_x A_x.$$

The sentence $\bigcap_x A_x$ is understood to be true if and only if A_x is true for every x of the range and $\bigcup_x A_x$ is true if and only if there exists at least one x of the range for which A_x is true. The symbol $\bigcap_x$ is called the *universal quantifier* and $\bigcup_x$ is called the *existential quantifier*. When the range of x is finite, Theorem 7 implies that

$$\sim \bigcap_x A_x = \bigcup_x \sim A_x \quad \text{and} \quad \sim \bigcup_x A_x = \bigcap_x \sim A_x.$$

We assume that the quantifiers are so interpreted that these equations hold even when the range of x is infinite.

Next let us study the concept of implication. We assume that the sentence "if A then B" has the same meaning as the sentence "A implies B" and we denote this sentence by $A \Rightarrow B$. We can doubtless agree that if A is true and $A \Rightarrow B$ is true, then B must be true and hence $A \Rightarrow B$ must be false whenever A is true and B is false. The other possibilities are not so obvious and hence we consider an example. One of the postulates defining the relation $<$ is the sentence "for every real number x and every real number y if $x < y$, then $x \neq y$." This sentence can be symbolized as follows:

$$\bigcap_{x \epsilon C} \bigcap_{x \epsilon C} (x < y) \Rightarrow (x \neq y).$$

We let $A = (x < y)$, $B = (x \neq y)$ and call A the hypothesis and B the conclusion. Then the implication $A \Rightarrow B$ is required to hold for every pair of real numbers x, y. It must hold when $x < y$ (for example, when $x = 1, y = 2$), when $y < x$ (for example, when $x = 2, y = 1$) and when $x = y$ (for example, when $x = 1 = y$). In the first and second cases B is true. In the second and third cases A is false and in these latter cases the implication is said to hold *vacuously*. Thus the implication $A \Rightarrow B$ must be true whenever B is true or A is false, i.e., whenever $B \cup \sim A$ is true. If $B \cup \sim A$ is false, then $\sim (B \cup \sim A) = A \cap \sim B$ is true, i.e., A is true and B is false and we have already agreed that in this case $A \Rightarrow B$ is false. It follows that if implication is so defined as to be satisfactory when applied to the above postulate, then it must be defined by the equation

$$(A \Rightarrow B) = (B \cup \sim A).$$

This equation defines what is called *material implication*. This implication is characterized by the requirement that it must hold if the conclusion is true or the hypothesis is false. Of course, the above is just one example, but it is advisable to assign the same meaning to implication every time it is used in the statement of a postulate and this meaning must be satisfactory in every case—in particular, in the above example. There are other types of implication, but material implication is the one found appropriate for the statements of postulates and theorems. Thus far, it has proved very satisfactory for such uses.

Material implication has the following property:

$$(A \Rightarrow B) = (\sim B \Rightarrow \sim A).$$

That is, A implies B if and only if *not* B implies *not* A. This is proved as follows.

$$(A \Rightarrow B) = (B \cup \sim A) = ((\sim A) \cup \sim (\sim B)) = (\sim B \Rightarrow \sim A).$$

Recall that $\varnothing$ denotes a contradiction and E denotes a tautology or trivially true sentence. It is not difficult to show that material implication has the following properties:

$$\text{If } A \cap \sim B = \varnothing, \quad \text{then} \quad A \Rightarrow B = E,$$

$$A \Rightarrow A = E,$$

$$(A \Rightarrow B) \cap (B \Rightarrow C) \cap \sim (A \Rightarrow C) = \varnothing,$$

$$[(A \Rightarrow B) \cap (B \Rightarrow C)] \Rightarrow (A \Rightarrow C) = E.$$

When $A \Rightarrow B$ is true, then B is necessarily true whenever A is true and in this case B is said to be a *necessary condition* for A. When $B \Rightarrow A$ is true, then the truth of B is sufficient to insure the truth of A and in this case B is said to be a *sufficient condition* for A. When both $A \Rightarrow B$ and $B \Rightarrow A$, then B is said to be a *necessary and sufficient condition* for A. In this case A and B are regarded as equivalent and we write $A \Leftrightarrow B$. We interpret $A \Leftrightarrow B$ as the sentence "A if and only if B."

It remains to state what is meant by the words "true" and "false" as they are used in mathematics. When we are discussing a particular mathematical system, we agree that the postulates and all of their consequences are true. However, this is not absolute truth but truth relative to the system. A proposition can be true in one system and false in another. For example, the commutative law for a product, i.e., $xy = yx$, is true for the number system but false if x and y are interpreted as matrices. A postulate system can be regarded as an elaborate definition. It indicates which system is under discussion by telling what properties are true of that system. The consequences of the postulates give amplifications of the meaning.

Let us see how logic can aid in the understanding of continuity and uniform continuity. First note that the sentence "$|f(x)-f(x_0)|<\varepsilon$ whenever $|x-x_0|<\delta$" means

$$|x-x_0|<\delta \Rightarrow |f(x)-f(x_0)|<\varepsilon,$$

and that this in turn means

$$(|f(x)-f(x_0)|<\varepsilon) \cup \sim(|x-x_0|<\delta).$$

Let C be the set of all real numbers and P be the set of all positive numbers. Then f is continuous at x_0 if and only if

$$\bigcap_{\varepsilon\in P} \bigcup_{\delta\in P} \bigcap_{x\in C} (|f(x)-f(x_0)|<\varepsilon) \cup \sim(|x-x_0|<\delta).$$

This function is discontinuous at x_0 if and only if

$$\sim \bigcap_{\varepsilon\in P} \bigcup_{\delta\in P} \bigcap_{x\in C} (|f(x)-f(x_0)|<\varepsilon) \cup \sim(|x-x_0|<\delta)$$

$$= \bigcup_{\varepsilon\in P} \bigcap_{\delta\in P} \bigcup_{x\in C} \sim(((|f(x)-f(x_0)|<\varepsilon) \cup \sim(|x-x_0|<\delta)))$$

$$= \bigcup_{\varepsilon\in P} \bigcap_{\delta\in P} \bigcap_{x\in C} (\sim(|f(x)-f(x_0)|<\varepsilon)) \cap (|x-x_0|<\delta).$$

Since $\sim(|f(x)-f(x_0)|<\varepsilon)$ means $|f(x)-f(x_0)|\geqslant\varepsilon$, the function is discontinuous at x_0 if there is a positive ε such that for every positive δ there exists an x for which $|f(x)-f(x_0)|\geqslant\varepsilon$ and $|x-x_0|<\delta$. An alternative interpretation is instructive. First note that the inequality $|x-x_0|<\delta$ means that x is in the interval having its center at x_0 and extending from $x_0-\delta$ to $x_0+\delta$. Thus the function is discontinuous at x_0 if there exists a positive ε such that every interval with center at x_0 contains an x for which $|f(x)-f(x_0)|\geqslant\varepsilon$.

Usually δ depends on ε and also on x_0. However, it sometimes happens that for a given interval I there exists a δ such that the inequality $|x - x_0| < \delta$ implies that $|f(x) - f(x_0)| < \varepsilon$ for every x_0 in I and that this is the case for every positive ε. We then say that the function is uniformly continuous in I. Thus f is uniformly continuous in I if and only if

$$\bigcap_{\varepsilon \in P} \bigcup_{\delta \in P} \bigcap_{x_0 \in I} \bigcap_{x \in C} (|f(x) - f(x_0)| < \varepsilon) \cup \sim (|x - x_0| < \delta).$$

2

On the Elementary

Transcendental Functions

JULIAN D. MANCILL

UNIVERSITY OF ALABAMA

Julian D. Mancill was born in Alabama, did his under-graduate work at the University of Alabama, and earned his Doctorate at the University of Chicago in 1934. At present Professor in the Department of Mathematics at his Alma Mater, he has also served at the Redstone Arsenal, University of Florida, and the University of South Carolina. His principal research interests are basic concepts and the calculus of variations. He is the author of *Modern Analytic Trigonometry*, and co-author with M. O. Gonzales of *Modern College Algebra*, *Basic College Algebra*, and *Contemporary Mathematics*.

In the following paper Professor Mancill develops the theory of the exponential, logarithmic, trigonometric, and inverse-trigonometric functions in a manner that is probably new to the reader. The approach may provide new insights, and it is consistent with techniques frequently used to define and develop the theory of other special functions.

ON THE ELEMENTARY
TRANSCENDENTAL FUNCTIONS

Julian D. Mancill

1. INTRODUCTION

The first examples of functions encountered by students in elementary mathematics belong to the class called the *elementary functions*. They are generally classified into two classes, namely, *elementary algebraic functions* and *elementary transcendental functions*. The elementary algebraic functions are defined in terms of basic algebraic operations and their treatment is gradually developed as the student progresses in his study of mathematics. For example, the expressions

$$x^2, \quad \sqrt{x}, \quad x^{11/17}, \quad \sqrt{1 - x^{1/2}},$$

determine elementary algebraic functions of the real variable x. This class of elementary functions is so broad and varied in complexity that students and writers have little difficulty in establishing examples of such functions as illustrations at any level. Thus, certain basic difficulties in the formulation of the whole class

Based in part on the author's article," The sine and cosine functions," *Mathematics Magazine*, Vol. 36, 1963, by permission of the Editor.

can be postponed until the student has reached a level of mathematical maturity sufficient to treat adequately this class of functions as a whole.

The elementary transcendental functions, on the other hand, are not so easily illustrated in elementary mathematics. They are the *exponential* and *logarithmic functions*, and the *trigonometric* and *inverse-trigonometric functions*. Examples, respectively, of these functions are denoted by the following well-known symbols:

$$2^x, \quad \log_a x, \quad \sin x, \quad \arcsin x,$$

where x is a real variable. Unfortunately, our familiarity with these symbols harbors basic difficulties in their complete formulation. Also, their variety is limited in comparison with the class of algebraic functions and, consequently, one must face these difficulties from the beginning. This presents a difficult pedagogical problem which is not always overcome in elementary mathematics texts. Our main purpose in this discussion is to present a development of each subclass of transcendental functions as outlined above at the basic calculus level which is elementary, brief, and complete.

2. EXPONENTIAL FUNCTIONS

The classical approach to the establishment of the elementary exponential functions a^x, where a is any positive real number and x is a real variable, is to define the system of positive integral exponents first, then extend this system by definitions to include, in turn, integral exponents, rational exponents, and real exponents. Perhaps this should be the method used to introduce these functions prior to calculus, but to do so completely is a long, tedious, and difficult task. Consequently, much of the basic material is slighted, and there results a treatment which is far from satisfactory. This is especially true of the extension from rational exponents to real exponents. We present a treatment here in terms of basic calculus which completely characterizes these functions, and which leads quickly to their desired properties.

We assume, for the moment, that there exists a real valued function $E(x)$ of the real variable x, with domain all real numbers, satisfying the following two postulates:

Postulate 1: $E(x) \cdot E(y) = E(x + y)$.

Postulate 2: $\lim\limits_{x \to 0^+} \dfrac{E(x) - 1}{x} = 1.$

It will be shown how these two simple postulates completely characterize a unique function $E(x)$ which is identical to the classical exponential function e^x referred to above for $a = e = 2.71828\ldots$.

Theorem 1. $\lim\limits_{x \to 0} \dfrac{E(x) - 1}{x} = 1.$

First, we note that

$$\lim_{x \to 0^+} E(x) = 1,$$

as follows from Postulate 2 and the properties of limits, since

$$\frac{E(x) - 1}{x} = 1 + \varepsilon \qquad \text{or} \qquad E(x) = 1 + x(1 + \varepsilon),$$

where $\varepsilon \to 0$ as $x \to 0^+$. The theorem follows from Postulate 2 and

$$\lim_{x \to 0^+} \frac{E(x) - 1}{x} = \lim_{x \to 0^+} \frac{E(-x) - 1}{-x} = \lim_{x \to 0^+} \frac{E(x) - 1}{x} \cdot \frac{1}{E(x)} = 1$$

because it is easily shown that $E(-x) = 1/E(x)$.

Theorem 2. $\dfrac{dE(x)}{dx} = E(x)\,for\ all\ values\ of\ x.$

This follows easily from the definition of a derivative and the above properties, since

$$\frac{dE(x)}{dx} = \lim_{h \to 0} \frac{E(x + h) - E(x)}{h} = E(x) \lim_{h \to 0} \frac{E(h) - 1}{h} = E(x).$$

Since every differentiable function is continuous, we have the following:

Corollary.   The function $E(x)$ is continuous for all values of x.

As another illustration of the proofs of the properties of $E(x)$, we prove the following theorem:

Theorem 3.   The function $E(x)$ is positive for all values of x.

From Theorem 1, we have

$$E(x) = 1 + x(1 + \varepsilon),$$

where $\varepsilon \to 0$ as $x \to 0$. Therefore, $E(x) \to 1$ as $x \to 0$ and there is an interval $[-\delta, \delta]$ on which $E(x) > 0$. For every x and y in this interval $E(x)$ and $E(y)$ are both positive, and we have

$$E(x) \cdot E(y) = E(x + y) > 0.$$

Consequently, $E(x) > 0$ on the interval $[-2\delta, 2\delta]$. Continuing this argument, we see that the theorem is true.

Theorem 4.   The function $E(x)$ satisfying Postulates 1 and 2 is unique.

Suppose there are two distinct functions $E_1(x)$ and $E_2(x)$ satisfying these two postulates. Then, since $dE_1(x)/dx = E_1'(x) = E_1$, $dE_2(x)/dx = E_2'(x) = E_2$, and $E_2(x) \neq 0$, we have

$$\frac{d(E_1/E_2)}{dx} = \frac{E_1'E_2 - E_1E_2'}{E_2^2} = \frac{E_1E_2 - E_1E_2}{E_2^2} \equiv 0,$$

and, consequently,

$$E_1/E_2 \equiv c,$$

where c is a constant. But it follows from Postulate 2 and the continuity of E_1 and E_2 that

$$E_1(0) = E_2(0) = 1.$$

Therefore, $c = 1$, and we have $E_1(x) \equiv E_2(x)$.

The existence of a function $E(x)$ satisfying our Postulates 1 and 2 can be shown directly by means of the series

$$E(x) = 1 + x + \frac{x^2}{2!} + \frac{x^3}{3!} + \cdots + \frac{x^n}{n!} + \cdots, \quad n = 0, 1, 2, \ldots,$$

which converges for all values of x. It is easily proved that the function defined by this formula satisfies our two postulates, and it is the only such function in view of the uniqueness property.

Now, the classical exponential function e^x referred to above can be shown to have properties 1 and 2 (postulates). Therefore, $E(x) \equiv e^x$ for all values of x as follows from the uniqueness property. Consequently, we are assured of the existence of such a function and we shall employ the latter notation from this point on.

It can now be shown that all the familiar properties of e^x can be derived from Postulates 1 and 2 without resort to the classical definition referred to above. Thus, these two simple postulates do completely characterize the function e^x.

In terms of the familiar language of college algebra, we say that e^x is the *power* of the *base e* and *exponent x*, thus indicating the name of exponential function with base e. We summarize the basic laws of exponents of base e in the next theorem, leaving their justification to the reader.

Theorem 5. The function e^x obeys the following laws of exponents:

(1) $e^x \cdot e^y = e^{x+y}$ (2) $e^0 = 1$

(3) $e^{-x} = 1/e^x$ (4) $e^x/e^y = e^{x-y}.$

Note that the familiar law of exponents $(e^x)^y = e^{xy}$, for example, is missing from the list in the last theorem. This is due to the fact that $(e^x)^y$ has not been defined. This we now proceed to do.

We now know that the function determined by the equation $y = e^x$ is a one-to-one mapping from the domain of all real numbers to the range of all positive real numbers because its derivative e^x is positive for all values of x. Consequently, the equation

$$a = e^k$$

has a unique solution k for each positive value of a, and we give

DEFINITION 1: $a^x = e^{kx}$, *for all values of* x.

Now, by means of the properties of e^x and Definition 1, we can derive all the properties of a^x, for example, the familiar ones in the next theorem.

Theorem 6. *General Laws of Exponents: The function* a^x, $a > 0$, *and* x *real has the following properties:*

(1) $a^x \cdot a^y = a^{x+y}$ (2) $(a^x)^y = a^{xy}$

(3) $a^0 = 1$ (4) $a^{-x} = \dfrac{1}{a^x}$

(5) $(ab)^x = a^x b^x$ (6) $\left(\dfrac{a}{b}\right)^x = \dfrac{a^x}{b^x}$

As an illustration, we shall prove property (2) and leave the others for the reader. From Definition 1, we have

$$a^x = e^{kx} = a_1$$

for each value of x. Therefore, we can write

$$(a^x)^y = a_1^y = e^{k_1 y}$$

for all values of y for each value of x. But if we let $y = 1$, we obtain

$$(a^x)^1 = a^x = e^{kx} = a_1 = e^{k_1},$$

and thus, $k_1 = kx$ for each value of x. It follows that

$$(a^x)^y = e^{k_1 y} = e^{kxy} = a^{xy}.$$

For convenience, we shall postpone the completion of the calculus of the exponential function a^x until after the treatment of logarithms in the next section.

3. LOGARITHMIC FUNCTIONS

Since the function defined by the equation $y = a^x$, $a > 0$, $a \neq 1$, is a continuous one-to-one mapping from the domain of all real numbers to the range of all positive real numbers, its inverse relation denoted by $x = \log_a y$ is a continuous function. To obtain an explicit expression for this inverse function, we see that

$$dy/dx = d\ e^{kx}/dx = ke^{kx} = ka^x = ky,$$

or

$$dx = \frac{1}{k}\frac{dy}{y}, \qquad y > 0, \qquad k \neq 0,$$

from which it follows that

$$\log_a y = x = \frac{1}{k}\int_1^y \frac{dy}{y}, \qquad y > 0, \qquad k \neq 0.$$

This is motivation for

DEFINITION 2: $\log_a y = \dfrac{1}{k}\displaystyle\int_1^y \dfrac{dy}{y}, \qquad y > 0, \qquad k \neq 0,$

where $\log_a y$ *denotes the logarithm of* y *to the base* a.

In particular, if $k = 1$, then the resulting function is called the *natural logarithm of* y which is denoted by

$$\ln y = \int_1^y \frac{dy}{y}, \qquad y > 0.$$

Thus, we see that

$$\log_a y = \frac{1}{k}\ln y, \qquad k \neq 0,$$

which proves the following theorem:

Theorem 7. In the definition $a^x = e^{kx}$,

$$k = \ln a \qquad or \qquad a^x = e^{k\ln a},$$

and, consequently,

$$\log_a y = \ln y / \ln a$$

for $a > 0$ and $a \neq 1$.

Now, all the properties of the logarithmic function $\log_a y$ can be derived from the basic ones given here, as, for example, those familiar ones in the next theorem.

Theorem 8. *Laws of Logarithms: The logarithmic function* $\log_a x$, $a > 0$, $a \neq 1$, *and* $x > 0$ *has the properties:*
    (1) $\log_a (x \cdot y) = \log_a x + \log_a y$
    (2) $\log_a (x/y) = \log_a x - \log_a y$
    (3) $\log_a (y)^x = x \log_a y$.
To prove (1), we let

$$M = \log_a x \qquad \text{or} \qquad x = a^M,$$

and

$$N = \log_a y \qquad \text{or} \qquad y = a^N.$$

Then, it follows that

$$x \cdot y = a^M \cdot a^N = a^{M+N}.$$

Therefore, we have

$$\log_a (x \cdot y) = M + N = \log_a x + \log_a y.$$

Proof of (2) is very similar and will be left to the reader. To prove (3), we have

$$\log_a y^x = \log_a e^{x \ln y} = \frac{1}{\ln a} \ln e^{x \ln y} = x \frac{\ln y}{\ln a} = x \log_a y.$$

We are now in position to establish the formula

$$e = \lim_{x \to 0} (1 + x)^{1/x}$$

by evaluating this limit directly by means of the above properties because

$$\lim_{x \to 0} (1 + x)^{1/x} = \lim_{x \to 0} e^{(1/x)\ln(1+x)} = \lim_{x \to 0} e^{[\ln(1+x)-\ln(1)]/x} = e^1 = e,$$

since e^x is continuous and $de^x/dx = e^x = 1$ for $x = 0$.

In the classical development of the exponential function e^x referred to in Section 2, the number e is defined by the formula

$$e = \lim_{n \to +\infty} \left(1 + \frac{1}{n}\right)^n \qquad (n = 1, 2, 3, \ldots).$$

This definition is consistent with the above formula and it can be used to obtain rational approximations to e. However, since n must be so large for this formula to give useful approximations, other methods have been developed in the past. But with the aid of the high-speed computers of today, the value of n required to obtain a desired approximation to e is of little concern and, consequently, this formula can be employed to obtain $e = 2.71828\ldots$ to any number of correct digits.

Numerical values of $\ln x$ can be obtained from the definition

$$\ln x = \int_1^x \frac{dy}{y}$$

by means of approximation methods in numerical analysis. Also, numerical values of $\ln x$ and e^x can be obtained from their series representations in calculus. After numerical values of $\ln x$ are determined, numerical values of $\log_a x$ are obtained by means of the change of base formula

$$\log_a x = \ln x / \ln a.$$

Numerical values of $a^x (a > 0)$ are obtained from those of e^x by means of the definition

$$a^x = e^{x \ln a}.$$

In order to construct accurate graphs of the functions a^x and $\log_a x$, we need the following obvious properties:

$$\lim_{x \to -\infty} a^x = \begin{cases} 0, & a > 1 \\ +\infty, & a < 1 \end{cases}, \qquad \lim_{x \to +\infty} a^x = \begin{cases} +\infty, & a > 1 \\ 0, & a < 1 \end{cases}$$

and

$$\lim_{x \to 0^+} \log_a x = \begin{cases} -\infty, & a > 1 \\ +\infty, & a < 1 \end{cases}, \qquad \lim_{x \to +\infty} \log_a x = \begin{cases} +\infty, & a > 1 \\ -\infty, & a < 1 \end{cases}.$$

Figures 2-1 and 2-2 are representative graphs of the exponential functions a^x and the logarithmic functions $\log_a x$, in Euclidean analytic geometry, for $a > 1$, $a = 1$, and $a < 1$. It must be noted that $\log_a x$ has not been defined for $a = 1$. However, the equation

$$x = 1^y$$

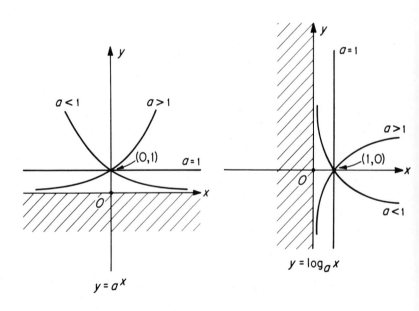

$$y = a^x$$

$$y = \log_a x$$

FIG. 2-1　　　　　　　　　　　　　　FIG. 2-2

has as solution set all pairs $(1, y)$. Therefore, the locus of this equation is the line $x = 1$ as shown in Figure 2-2. Consequently, $\log_1 x$ can have meaning only when $x = 1$, and then y is arbitrary. This concept has little value other than to explain why the line $x = 1$ can be thought of as a limiting case of the loci of the functions $y = \log_a x$ as $a \to 1$.

We close this discussion of the exponential and logarithmic functions with the remark that the calculus of these functions can be completed naturally and easily. This is one of the rewards derived from our approach to these functions. Some of these rewards could be realized by a combination of the classical and present treatments of the exponential and logarithmic functions. That is, one could define a^x as usual, derive properties 1 and 2, and then make use of these properties as presented here.

4. THE SINE AND COSINE FUNCTIONS

Traditionally, the trigonometric functions have been characterized as functions of angle measure in Euclidean geometry. This is the natural and historical development of the trigonometric functions relating to their application to triangle measurement and perhaps this should be the method used to introduce trigonometry. However, many writers have attempted to free the trigonometric functions from the concept of angle measure by defining them as functions of the set of real numbers representing the arc length along the unit circle measured from a fixed point on the circle. Such a procedure merely shifts the emphasis from angle measure in radians to the measure of arc length along the unit circle, both measures being represented by the same set of real numbers. However, it is desirable for many of the applied sciences, as well as for " pure " analysis, to have the trigonometric functions defined as functions of a real variable, free of any prescribed two-dimensional metric. This we propose to do in a very elementary way.

We shall employ a postulational development of these functions by assuming the existence, for the moment, of a pair of real valued functions sin x and cos x with the following three properties:

Postulate 3: $\sin(x - y) = \sin x \cos y - \cos x \sin y,$

Postulate 4: $\cos(x - y) = \cos x \cos y + \sin x \sin y,$

Postulate 5: $\displaystyle \lim_{x \to 0^+} \frac{\sin x}{x} = 1,$

where x and y are real variables with domains of all real numbers. It will be shown that these postulates define a unique pair of functions sin x and cos x. Then it is obvious that the one-parameter family of pairs of functions, sin (kx) and cos (kx), have properties 3 and 4, and

Postulate 5′: $\displaystyle \lim_{x \to 0^+} \frac{\sin (kx)}{x} = k \lim_{x \to 0^+} \frac{\sin (kx)}{kx} = k > 0,$

for each real positive value of k. Thus, we shall show the existence of a one-parameter family of pairs of sine and cosine functions with domains of all real numbers which have all the properties of the classical sine and cosine functions of angle measure in trigonometry. Then we shall identify sin (kx) and cos (kx), for each value of k, with their circular function counterparts in trigonometry, where the value of k is determined by the unit of angle measure employed in defining the circular functions.

We shall derive some of the familiar properties of sin x and cos x from Postulates 3, 4, and 5 without further definitions. Then it follows easily from Postulates 3, 4, and 5′ that the functions sin (kx) and cos (kx) have corresponding properties for each value of k.

$$\sin 0 = 0. \tag{i}$$

This property follows from Postulate 3 for $x = y$.

$$\cos 0 = 1. \tag{ii}$$

If we set $y = 0$ in Postulate 3, we have

$$\sin x = \sin x \cos 0,$$

or

$$\sin x(1 - \cos 0) = 0$$

for all values of x. However, it follows from Postulate 5 that there are values of x for which $\sin x \neq 0$. Therefore, $1 - \cos 0$ must be zero and

$$\cos 0 = 1.$$

$$\sin^2 x + \cos^2 x \equiv 1. \tag{iii}$$

This follows immediately from Postulate 4 and (ii) for $y = x$.

$$\sin(-y) \equiv -\sin y. \tag{iv}$$

If we set $x = 0$ in Postulate 3, we obtain

$$\sin(-y) \equiv \sin 0 \cos y - \cos 0 \sin y \equiv -\sin y.$$

In the same way we can prove that

$$\cos(-y) \equiv \cos y. \tag{v}$$

$$\sin(x + y) \equiv \sin x \cos y + \cos x \sin y. \tag{vi}$$

This property follows from

$$\sin(x + y) \equiv \sin[x - (-y)]$$

and the preceding properties. In a similar way we can prove

$$\cos(x + y) \equiv \cos x \cos y - \sin x \sin y. \tag{vii}$$

Now, all the other well-known identities of trigonometry can be easily derived for $\sin x$ and $\cos x$ in terms of the basic ones derived here. As an example, we have

$$\sin x - \sin y \equiv 2 \cos \frac{x + y}{2} \sin \frac{x - y}{2}, \tag{viii}$$

whose proof may be constructed or found in texts on trigonometry.

We next develop some of the calculus of the sine and cosine functions.

Theorem 9. $\lim\limits_{x \to 0} \dfrac{\sin x}{x} = 1$ *and* $\lim\limits_{x \to 0} \dfrac{\sin(kx)}{x} = k.$

The first of these limits follows from Postulate 5 and (iv), and the second from Postulate 5′ and (iv).

Theorem 10.   Sin x *is continuous at* $x = 0.$
From the definition of limit and (viii), we note that

$$\frac{\sin x}{x} = 1 + \varepsilon,$$

where $\varepsilon \to 0$ as $x \to 0$, from which it follows that

$$\sin x = x(1 + \varepsilon).$$

Therefore, we have

$$\lim_{x \to 0} \sin x = 0 = \sin 0,$$

and the property is proved.

Theorem 11.   Sin x *and* cos x *are continuous everywhere.*
To prove this we shall make use of the relation

$$\sin x_1 - \sin x_2 \equiv 2 \left| \sin \frac{x_1 - x_2}{2} \right| \cdot \left| \cos \frac{x_1 + x_2}{2} \right|.$$

Since

$$|\cos x| \leqslant 1,$$

we have

$$|\sin x_1 - \sin x_2| \leqslant M \left| \sin \frac{x_1 - x_2}{2} \right|,$$

where M is a positive constant, which proves our property in view of Theorem 10. The continuity of cos x follows from a similar argument.

Theorem 12. *Sin x and cos x are differentiable with*

$$\frac{d}{dx}(\sin x) = \cos x \qquad and \qquad \frac{d}{dx}(\cos x) = -\sin x.$$

We have

$$\frac{d}{dx}(\sin x) = \lim_{h \to 0} \frac{\sin(x+h) - \sin x}{h} = \lim_{h \to 0} \frac{2 \sin(h/2)\cos(x+h/2)}{h}$$

$$= \lim_{h \to 0} \frac{\sin h/2}{h/2} \cdot \lim_{h \to 0} \cos(x+h/2)$$

$$= \cos x,$$

as follows from Postulate 5 and the continuity of cos x. Proof of the second part can be made in a similar way.

We can now prove the uniqueness property.

Theorem 13. *The functions $\sin x$ and $\cos x$ satisfying Postulates 3, 4, and 5 are unique.*

To prove this property we suppose there are two pairs of functions $\sin_1 x$, $\cos_1 x$ and $\sin_2 x$, $\cos_2 x$ satisfying our postulates for all values of x. Now we define the function

$$f(x) \equiv (\sin_1 x - \sin_2 x)^2 + (\cos_1 x - \cos_2 x)^2,$$

which is differentiable for all values of x, and

$$f'(x) = 2(\sin_1 x - \sin_2 x)(\cos_1 x - \cos_2 x)$$
$$+ 2(\cos_1 x - \cos_2 x)(-\sin_1 x + \sin_2 x) \equiv 0.$$

Therefore, $f(x)$ is a constant and if we evaluate it at $x = 0$, we obtain

$$f(0) = f(x) \equiv 0.$$

Thus, we have

$$\sin_1 x \equiv \sin_2 x \qquad \text{and} \qquad \cos_1 x \equiv \cos_2 x.$$

Up to this point, we have not faced the problem of showing there exists a pair of functions sin x and cos x satisfying our postulates. To accomplish this we shall show that the functions

$$S(x) = x - \frac{x^3}{3!} + \cdots + (-1)^n \frac{x^{2n+1}}{(2n+1)!} + \cdots$$

and

$$C(x) = 1 - \frac{x^2}{2!} + \cdots + (-1)^n \frac{x^{2n}}{(2n)!} + \cdots$$

satisfy our postulates and, therefore, must be the functions we are seeking, since there is only one pair by the uniqueness property. That these infinite series define functions of x for all real values of x follows from well-known properties of such series.

Postulate 5 is satisfied by $S(x)$ because

$$\lim_{x \to 0} \frac{S(x)}{x} = \lim_{x \to 0} \left(1 - \frac{x^2}{3!} + \cdots \right) = 1.$$

We could show that Postulates 3 and 4 are satisfied by this pair of functions by direct substitution and operations on infinite series, but we shall follow a method similar to that in the proof of Theorem 13. First we note that

$$\frac{dS(x)}{dx} = 1 - \frac{x^2}{2!} + \cdots = C(x)$$

and

$$\frac{dC(x)}{dx} = -x + \frac{x^3}{3!} - \cdots = -S(x)$$

from known properties of series.

Now we define the function

$$g(x) \equiv \{S(x - y) - [S(x)C(y) - C(x)S(y)]\}^2$$
$$+ \{C(x - y) - [C(x)C(y) + S(x)S(y)]\}^2 \equiv g_1^2(x) + g_2^2(x),$$

where we consider y to be a parameter. Differentiating $g(x)$ with respect to x, we have

$$g'(x) = 2g_1(x)\{C(x-y) - [C(x)C(y) + S(x)S(y)]\}$$
$$+ 2g_2(x)\{-S(x-y) - [-S(x)C(y) + C(x)S(y)]\}$$
$$= 2g_1(x)g_2(x) + 2g_2(x)[-g_1(x)] \equiv 0,$$

and it follows that $g(x)$ is a constant. Evaluating it as $x = 0$, we find

$$g(0) = g(x) \equiv 0,$$

from which it follows that $g_1(x) \equiv g_2(x) \equiv 0$ and Postulates 3 and 4 are satisfied.

Thus, we have exhibited the unique functions

$$\sin x \equiv S(x) \qquad \text{and} \qquad \cos x \equiv C(x),$$

which satisfy our postulates.

To complete our formulation of the properties of the functions $\sin x$ and $\cos x$ from our postulates we need to derive their periodic and other numerical properties. We shall not accomplish this in its entirety here because we shall identify these functions with the circular sine and cosine functions of radian measure of angles developed in trigonometry, and their numerical properties will follow because of the uniqueness property. However, we shall derive their periodic property.

First, we shall locate the first positive zero of $\cos x$. To do this we shall make use of the fact that the terms in the series expression for $\sin x$ and $\cos x$ may be rearranged in any manner without affecting their properties. Thus, we see that

$$\cos x = \left(1 - \frac{x^2}{2!}\right) + \frac{x^4}{4!}\left(1 - \frac{x^2}{30}\right) + \cdots$$

in which for each value of x the terms, beyond a certain point, are all positive. Therefore, we have

$$\cos x > 1 - \frac{x^2}{2!}, \qquad 0 < x^2 < 30.$$

For example, these conditions are fulfilled if $x = \sqrt{2}$ and, therefore,

$$\cos \sqrt{2} > 0.$$

Also, there is no zero of $\cos x$ between 0 and $\sqrt{2}$.

Next let us regroup the terms of the series as follows:

$$\cos x = 1 - \left(\frac{x^2}{2!} - \frac{x^4}{4!}\right) - \left(\frac{x^6}{6!} - \frac{x^8}{8!}\right) - \cdots ,$$

from which it follows that

$$\cos x < 1 - \frac{x^2}{2!}\left(1 - \frac{x^2}{12}\right), \qquad 0 < x^2 < 56,$$

and in particular

$$\cos \sqrt{3} < -\frac{1}{8} < 0.$$

Thus, we have shown that $\cos x$ has at least one zero on the interval $\sqrt{2} < x < \sqrt{3}$ because it is continuous and changes sign on this interval. Now we wish to show that there is just one zero on this interval.

First, we see that $\sin x > 0$ for $\sqrt{2} \leqslant x \leqslant \sqrt{3}$ from

$$\sin x = x\left(1 - \frac{x^2}{3!}\right) + \frac{x^5}{5!}\left(1 - \frac{x^2}{42}\right) + \cdots$$

$$> x\left(-\frac{x^2}{6}\right), \qquad 0 < x^2 < 42.$$

Therefore,

$$\frac{d \cos x}{dx} = -\sin x < 0, \qquad \sqrt{2} < x < \sqrt{3},$$

and there is exactly one zero of $\cos x$ on this interval which we shall momentarily denote by z. It follows that

$$\cos z = 0 \qquad \text{and} \qquad \sin z = 1.$$

Now, from (vi) and (vii), we can write

$$\sin(x+z) = \sin x \cos z + \cos x \sin z = \cos x,$$

$$\sin(x+2z) = \sin[(x+z)+z] = \cos(x+z)$$

$$= \cos x \cos z - \sin x \sin z = -\sin x,$$

$$\sin(x+3z) = \sin[(x+z)+2z] = -\sin(x+z) = -\cos x,$$

$$\sin(x+4z) = \sin[(x+2z)+2z] = -\sin(x+2z) = \sin x,$$

for all values of x. In a similar way we can show that

$$\cos(x+4z) = \cos x.$$

From these relations we see that

$$\sin 2z = 0, \quad \cos 2z = 1, \quad \sin 3z = -1, \quad \cos 3z = 0.$$

It has just been shown that $\sin x$ and $\cos x$ are periodic with a period $4z$. Since these functions are continuous, they have a smallest positive period, and it follows from $\sin(x+z) = \cos x$ that they have the same smallest period, say p. We shall now show that $p = 4z$. Since

$$\sin(x+p) = \sin x$$

$$\cos(x+p) = \cos x$$

for all values of x, we have $\sin p = 0$ and $\cos p = 1$, for $x = 0$. Therefore,

$$\cos p = \cos^2 \frac{p}{2} - \sin^2 \frac{p}{2} = 1 \quad \text{and} \quad \cos^2 \frac{p}{2} + \sin^2 \frac{p}{2} = 1,$$

from which we obtain

$$\cos^2 \frac{p}{2} = 1 \quad \text{and} \quad \sin \frac{p}{2} = 0.$$

But $\cos p/2$ cannot be $+1$ with $\sin p/2 = 0$, for then $p/2$ would be a period and p would not be the minimum period. Consequently, we have

$$\sin \frac{p}{2} = 0 \quad \text{and} \quad \cos \frac{p}{2} = -1.$$

Now, with these properties, we have

$$\cos \frac{p}{2} = \cos^2 \frac{p}{4} - \sin^2 \frac{p}{4} = -1,$$

$$\cos^2 \frac{p}{4} + \sin^2 \frac{p}{4} = 1,$$

$$\cos \frac{p}{4} = 0.$$

Therefore, we have shown that $p/4 = z$ since z is the first positive zero of $\cos x$.

We have shown that the functions $\sin x$ and $\cos x$ oscillate periodically between $+1$ and -1, and it is easily seen that between these extreme values they are monotone because the sign of the derivative in each case is constant between these points.

For convenience, we shall postpone further development of these functions until we introduce their geometric interpretations.

5. THE INVERSE TRIGONOMETRIC FUNCTIONS

The function defined by the equation

$$y = \sin x, \qquad -z \leqslant x \leqslant z,$$

is continuous and strictly monotone increasing on its domain since $dy/dx = \cos x > 0$ on the open interval $-z < x < z$. Therefore, its inverse relation, denoted by

$$x = \arcsin y, \qquad -1 \leqslant y \leqslant 1,$$

is a function, which is continuous on its domain. The continuity of arcsin y can be shown directly by showing that for any value of y on $-1 \leqslant y \leqslant 1$ and h restricted so that $-1 \leqslant y + h \leqslant 1$, then

$$\lim_{h \to 0} [\text{arcsin } (y + h) - \text{arcsin } y] = 0.$$

Suppose we let

$$x_1 = \text{arcsin } (y + h) \qquad \text{or} \qquad \sin x_1 = y + h,$$

and

$$x_2 = \text{arcsin } y \qquad \text{or} \qquad \sin x_2 = y.$$

Then we have

$$\sin (x_1 - x_2) = \sin x_1 \cos x_2 - \cos x_1 \sin x_2$$

$$= (y + h)\sqrt{1 - y^2} - \sqrt{1 - (y + h)^2} \cdot y,$$

for all values of y and $y + h$ on the closed interval, and

$$\lim_{h \to 0} \sin (x_1 - x_2) = y\sqrt{1 - y^2} - y\sqrt{1 - y^2} = 0,$$

from which it follows that

$$x_1 \to x_2 \qquad \text{as} \qquad h \to 0.$$

Thus, the inverse function arcsin y is continuous on $-1 \leqslant y \leqslant 1$.

In order to obtain an explicit expression for this inverse function, we make use of (iii) and Theorem 12 to obtain

$$y'^2 + y^2 = 1,$$

from which we see that

$$dx = \pm \frac{dy}{\sqrt{1 - y^2}} \qquad \text{and} \qquad x = \pm \int_0^y \frac{dy}{\sqrt{1 - y^2}},$$

for $-1 < y < 1$. But it follows from our definition of arcsin $y = x$ that x and y must have the same sign for $-1 < y < 1$, and we have

$$\text{arcsin } y = \int_0^y \frac{dy}{\sqrt{1 - y^2}}, \qquad -1 < y < 1.$$

Although the last integral is improper at $y = -1$ and $y = 1$, it converges for these values of y, as follows from well-known tests for convergence of such integrals. Since arcsin y is continuous on the closed interval $-1 \leqslant y \leqslant 1$, it follows that this integral converges to $-z$ and $+z$ at -1 and $+1$, respectively. Therefore, we have

$$\arcsin y = \int_0^y \frac{dy}{\sqrt{1 - y^2}}, \qquad -1 \leqslant y \leqslant 1.$$

A very similar argument shows that if $y = \cos x$, $0 \leqslant x \leqslant 2z$, then

$$x = \arccos y = -\int_1^y \frac{dy}{\sqrt{1 - y^2}}, \qquad -1 \leqslant y \leqslant 1,$$

which is continuous and differentiable with

$$\frac{d(\arccos y)}{dy} = \frac{-1}{\sqrt{1 - y^2}}.$$

It is interesting to note that the value of z can now be approximated more accurately than $\sqrt{2} < z < \sqrt{3}$ given above. For, it is easily shown that

$$\sin \frac{z}{2} = \cos \frac{z}{2} = \frac{1}{\sqrt{2}}.$$

Consequently, we have

$$\frac{z}{2} = \int_0^{1/\sqrt{2}} \frac{dt}{\sqrt{1 - t^2}} = \arcsin \frac{1}{\sqrt{2}}.$$

from which $z/2$ can be approximated directly, resulting in

$$2z = 3.14159\ldots.$$

In the next section we shall show that $2z = \pi$, where π is the constant ratio of the circumference of a circle to its diameter in Euclidean geometry. Therefore, we could have taken $2z$ as the definition of π in the present context.

Now, the other trigonometric functions and their inverse

functions can be introduced in terms of the two functions $\sin x$ and $\cos x$. We shall not pursue this matter here because our purpose has been accomplished by the basic development of the sine and cosine functions.

By this time the reader may well have wondered why we chose the formulas in 3 and 4 as postulates rather than the formulas for $\sin(x+y)$ and $\cos(x+y)$. If we did assume the latter two formulas along with Postulate 5, the resulting functions $\sin x$ and $\cos x$ would not be unique. This is verified by observing that not only would these two functions have the three properties but so would the pair of functions $e^x \sin x$ and $e^x \cos x$.

Also, one may wonder if all three Postulates 3, 4, and 5 are necessary for our development; that is, can we get along with fewer postulates? The answer to this question is yes, because one can carry out the entire development, including a proof of Postulate 3, with Postulates 4 and 5. However, to do so would involve much more complex and advanced concepts.

6. GEOMETRIC INTERPRETATIONS

In order to identify the functions $\sin(kx)$ and $\cos(kx)$ with their circular function counterparts in trigonometry, we shall construct an interpretation in Euclidean geometry. To this end let us consider the equation

$$x^2 + y^2 = 1/k^2, \qquad k > 0$$

of the circle with center at the origin of the coordinate system and radius $1/k$. We shall make use of the following parametric representation of this circle:

$$x = \frac{1}{k} \cos(kt), \qquad y = \frac{1}{k} \sin(kt),$$

for each positive value of k, where $\sin(kt)$ and $\cos(kt)$ are the functions defined by Postulates 3, 4, and 5′ of Section 4. Now we note the following interesting property.

Theorem 14.　*The length of arc on the circle C with the radius* $1/k$ *from the point* $(1/k, 0)$ *to the point* $[(1/k) \cos (kT), (1/k) \sin (kT)]$ *is* T.

This follows easily from the formula for arc length in calculus, or it may be shown directly from the definition of arc length and the properties of the functions sin (kt) and cos (kt). Therefore, if on the circle C a point P is chosen with abscissa OA equal to $(1/k)$ cos (kT), then the ordinate AP is equal to $(1/k) \sin (kT)$ and the length of the circular arc BP is T. Consequently, if we let s denote the measure of the straight angle BOB' with respect to some arbitrary unit of angle measure, then from well-known properties of Euclidean geometry

$$\frac{\theta_s}{T} = \frac{s}{\pi/k} \qquad \text{or} \qquad \theta_s = \frac{ks}{\pi} T = \frac{s}{\pi} \frac{T}{r}, \qquad r = 1/k,$$

where θ_s denotes the measure (in s units) of the angle at the center of C subtended by the arc BP. Now if we choose

$$k = \pi/s,$$

then $\theta_s = T$ and the measure of the arc T equals that of the subtended angle for the circle with radius $r = 1/k = s/\pi$; that is, the number of linear units (π/sth part of the radius) in the length of the arc BP equals the number of units of angle measure (s units) of the subtended angle for the circle with radius $r = s/\pi$.

It follows, therefore, that we may take the length of arc T on this circle as the measure of the subtended angle in s units of angle measure. Thus, we have exhibited a measure function for angles in s units, simply the arc length function on the circle of radius $r = s/\pi$, and our three Postulates 3, 4, and 5′ insure the properties

$$\sin\left(\frac{\pi}{s} T\right) = \sin \theta_s = \frac{\pi}{s} y, \qquad \cos\left(\frac{\pi}{s} T\right) = \cos \theta_s = \frac{\pi}{s} x.$$

At the same time we have an identification of the functions sin (kx) and cos (kx) with the circular functions $\sin \theta_s$ and $\cos \theta_s$ for each

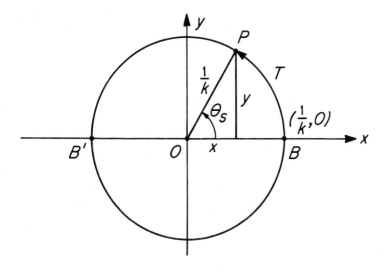

Fig. 2-3

value of $k = \pi/s$, all values of s, simply by interpreting the real variable x as the arc length T on the circle with radius $r = 1/k = s/\pi$. Therefore, we have all the numerical properties of $\sin (kx)$ and $\cos (kx)$ for each value of k, including their periodicity, from their circular function counterparts as follows from the uniqueness property. In this connection, we note the correspondence between the completion of the periods of $\sin x$ and $\cos x$ and the fact that at the same time the point P describes the circumference of the unit circle ($k = 1$). Therefore, we conclude that $p = 4z = 2\pi$ or $z = \pi/2$.

Conversely, we may consider the identifications

$$\sin \theta_s = \sin\left(\frac{\pi}{s} x\right) \qquad \text{and} \qquad \cos \theta_s = \cos\left(\frac{\pi}{s} x\right)$$

as interpretations of $\sin \theta_s$ and $\cos \theta_s$ as functions of angle measure θ_s. For example, for $s = \pi$ (radian measure), we make the identifications

$$\sin \theta_\pi = \sin x \qquad \text{and} \qquad \cos \theta_\pi = \cos x,$$

and for $s = 180$ (degree measure)

$$\sin \theta_{180} = \sin\left(\frac{\pi}{180}\, x\right) \qquad \text{and} \qquad \cos \theta_{180} = \cos\left(\frac{\pi}{180}\, x\right)$$

for all values of x. Consequently, when we define the sine and cosine functions of angle measure θ_s in trigonometry, these functions are unique for each unit of angle measure, but each unit gives rise to a different pair of functions of arc length which we have shown can be identified with one of the pairs of numerical functions (subsets of $R \times R$) in the family of pairs $\sin (kx)$ and $\cos (kx)$ determined axiomatically by Postulates 3, 4, and 5'. Thus, radian measure is not the only unit of angle measure which gives rise to numerical functions. However, the radian is the only unit of angle measure for which the measure of the angle and all the trigonometric functions of that measure can be represented by lengths employing the same unit of length, the radius of the unit circle. Therefore, radian measure of angles takes on a fundamental role in classical mathematics involving the trigonometric functions.

With these identifications, we can interpret the arithmetic operations on the trigonometric functions and their variables. For example, we have

$$\theta_s + \sin \theta_s = T + \sin\left(\frac{\pi}{s}\, T\right) = x + \sin\left(\frac{\pi}{s}\, x\right)$$

for all values of x for each value of s. Therefore, in particular

$$1° + \sin 1° = 1 + \sin\left(\frac{\pi}{180}\right) \doteq 1.0175, \text{ degree units,}$$

and

$$1_r + \sin 1_r = 1 + \sin 1 \doteq 1.8415, \text{ radian units.}$$

The classical development of the calculus of the circular functions in Euclidean geometry assumes the unit of angle measure to be the radian with attempts to prove the equality

$$\lim_{\theta_\pi \to 0} \frac{\sin \theta_\pi}{\theta_\pi} = 1.$$

Then the derivative formula for the sine function is derived. In so doing, the impression is often given that no other unit of measure can be employed. We shall emphasize that this is not the case by showing how one may obtain the derivative formulas for the cosine functions of angle measure in terms of an arbitrary unit of measure, without making use of the above limit. Thus, we will point out again that the use of radian measure is one of choice and not one of necessity.

First, we need to exhibit a workable measure function of Euclidean angles which establishes a one-to-one mapping from the set of all Euclidean angles to some interval of the real line. One such measure function was described above, the arc length along the circle of radius s/π. But if one pursues this representation of angle measure in terms of x and y in the equation of the circle, an improper integral enters, which is a rather advanced concept and is often omitted in short courses in calculus. Thus, we seek a measure function which avoids this problem. This leads us to a measure function in terms of the area of circular sectors with the corresponding central angles in standard position (see Figure 2-4).

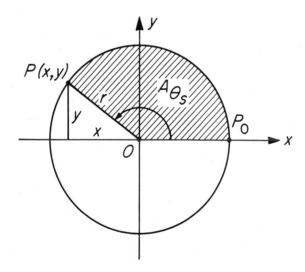

Fig. 2-4

We shall outline the derivation of such a measure function. Since the areas of any two sectors of the same circle are proportional to measures of the corresponding central angles, we have

$$A_{\theta_s}/\theta_s = \pi r^2/2s$$

or

$$\theta_s = 2sA_{\theta_s}/\pi r^2,$$

where s is the measure assigned to the straight angle, θ_s denotes the measure of the central angle, and A_{θ_s} denotes the area of the circular sector. Since $x^2 + y^2 = r^2$ on the circle under consideration, we have

$$\theta_s(x) = \frac{2s}{\pi r^2}\left[\int_x^r \sqrt{r^2 - t^2}\,dt + \frac{x}{2}\sqrt{r^2 - x^2}\right], \qquad -r \leqslant x \leqslant r,$$

as our *measure function of angles* P_0OP *determined by* x, including the null angle with measure $\theta_s(r) = 0$ and the straight angle with measure $\theta_s(-r) = s$, which can be shown to have the desired properties. That there is a single value of x on $-r \leqslant x \leqslant r$, and a corresponding unique angle, for each value of θ_s on $0 \leqslant \theta_s \leqslant s$ follows from

$$\frac{d\theta_s}{dx} = \frac{s}{\pi}\frac{1}{\sqrt{r^2 - x^2}} \neq 0, \qquad -r < x < r.$$

Thus, we have established a workable measure function of Euclidean angles and the null and straight angles. Consequently, we can assign a unique measure θ_s to any *general angle*, namely

$$\theta_s = n \times s + \alpha,$$

where n is an integer and $\alpha < s$ is the measure of a Euclidean angle or the null angle. Conversely, given any real numbers θ_s and $s > 0$, there exists a unique integer n and a unique positive real number $\alpha < s$ such that the above equality is true. In this way we can establish a one-to-one correspondence between general angles and the real numbers such that each real number represents the measure of a unique angle for each value of s.

Now we define

$$\sin \theta_s = y/r, \qquad \cos \theta_s = x/r,$$

for all values of θ_s. It follows from Theorem 11 that these two functions are continuous for all values of θ_s. This is true because the proof of this theorem is the same in the present context as that of Section 4, since only identity properties are employed.

Returning to the above formula for $d\theta_s/dx$, we have

$$\frac{d\theta_s}{dx} = -\frac{s}{\pi}\frac{1}{r \sin \theta_s}, \qquad 0 < \theta_s < s.$$

Therefore, it follows that

$$\frac{dx}{d\theta_s} = \frac{d(r \cos \theta_s)}{d\theta_s} = -\frac{\pi}{s} r \sin \theta_s,$$

or

$$\frac{d(\cos \theta_s)}{d\theta_s} = -\frac{\pi}{s} \sin \theta_s, \qquad 0 < \theta_s < s.$$

But the right-hand derivative of $\cos \theta_s$ at $\theta_s = 0$ is $-\pi/s \cdot \sin 0 = 0$ because

$$\lim_{h \to 0^+} \frac{\cos(0+h) - \cos 0}{h} = -\frac{\pi}{s} \lim_{h \to 0^+} \frac{h \sin(0+ht)}{h}, \qquad 0 < t < 1,$$

$$= -\frac{\pi}{s} \lim_{h \to 0^+} \sin(ht) = -\frac{\pi}{s} \sin 0 = 0,$$

as follows from the Theorem of the Mean and the continuity of $\sin \theta_s$ at $\theta_s = 0$. Since we know that $\cos(-\theta_s) = \cos \theta_s$, it follows that the left-hand derivative of $\cos \theta_s$ exists at $\theta_s = 0$ and equals zero there. Therefore, since $\cos \theta_s$ is continuous at $\theta_s = 0$, it has the derivative $-(\pi/s)\sin 0 = 0$ at $\theta_s = 0$.

A similar argument shows that the formula for $d(\cos \theta_s)/d\theta_s$ holds at $\theta_s = s$ and equals zero there. Therefore, we have derived this formula for $0 \leqslant \theta_s \leqslant s$. But in view of the periodicity properties of the sine and cosine functions, we have established our derivative formula for all values of θ_s for each fixed value of s.

Note, also, that our derivation of this derivative formula avoids the somewhat troublesome proof that

$$\lim_{\theta_\pi \to 0} \frac{\sin \theta_\pi}{\theta_\pi} = 1,$$

where θ_π is the radian measure of angles, needed in the classical proof of the formula. In the present treatment, this property follows from the derivative of $\sin \theta_\pi$ at $\theta_\pi = 0$.

Numerical values of the sine and cosine functions $\sin x = \sin \theta_\pi$ and $\cos x = \cos \theta_\pi$ can be obtained from the series $S(x)$ and $C(x)$ of Section 4. Then numerical values of any member of the family of functions $\sin \theta_s$ and $\cos \theta_s$ can be obtained from the relations

$$\sin \theta_s = \sin \left(\frac{s}{\pi} \theta_\pi \right) \qquad \text{and} \qquad \cos \theta_s = \cos \left(\frac{s}{\pi} \theta_\pi \right),$$

respectively.

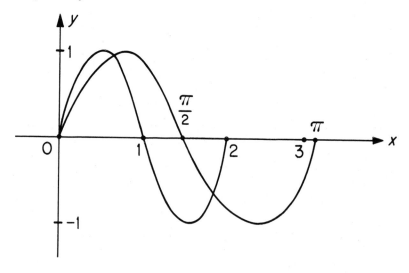

Fig. 2-5

Accurate graphs of these functions can be constructed for any unit of angle measure. Figure 2.5 gives the graphs of the functions defined by

$$y = \sin \theta_{\pi/2} \qquad \text{and} \qquad y = \sin \theta_1,$$

that is, for $s = \pi/2$ and $s = 1$, on $0 \leqslant \theta_s \leqslant 2s$ in each case.

The reader should attempt to sketch the graph of the function defined by

$$y = \sin \theta_{180}, \qquad 0 \leqslant \theta_{180} \leqslant 360,$$

on this coordinate system. To do so would require an extension of the x-axis to include 360 unit segments, or actually 30 feet. So, one begins to see the relationships between the graphs of these functions defined by various units of angle measure.

3

Areas and Volumes without Limit Processes

DONALD E. RICHMOND

WILLIAMS COLLEGE

Donald E. Richmond, Frederick Latimer Wells Professor at Williams College, took his Bachelor's and Master's Degrees in physics and his Ph.D. in mathematics at Cornell University in 1926. The following year he joined the faculty of Williams College, and served as Chairman of the Mathematics Department from 1940 to 1964. He has taught also at Cornell University, Massachusetts Institute of Technology, and Dartmouth College, as well as holding a National Research Fellowship at Harvard and attending the Institute for Advanced Study. He has been deeply involved in improving mathematical education at all levels by serving on committees, lecturing widely, and preparing new teaching materials. He was one of the initiators of the visiting lectureship program of the Mathematical Association of America and served as its chairman during the first three years. In 1958 he was awarded an honorary degree of Doctor of Science by Williams College. His research publications deal with the calculus of variations, quantum mechanics, and differential equations. He is the author of *The Dilemma of Modern Physics*, *Fundamentals of Calculus*, *Introductory Calculus*, and *Calculus with Analytic Geometry*.

In the following lecture Professor Richmond shows that the theory of limits is not at all necessary to a rigorous theory of a large part of elementary calculus.

AREAS AND VOLUMES WITHOUT
LIMIT PROCESSES

Donald E. Richmond

1. INTRODUCTION

It is universally believed that areas under non-linear graphs can be found only by some sort of limit process. This is not the case, 2,000 years of opinion to the contrary notwithstanding.

We shall assume as usual that the area of a plane region bounded by a simple closed curve is a positive number (positivity), that congruent regions have the same area, and that the area of the union of two non-overlapping regions is the sum of their areas (additivity). Finally, we assume that the area of a rectangle is the product of the length of its base by its altitude.

We begin with a simple case.

2. THE AREA UNDER A PARABOLA

Let $F(x)$ be the area under the parabola $y = x^2$ above the interval $[0, x]$, and $F(x')$ the area above $[0, x']$ $(x' > x)$. Then the area above $[x, x']$ is $F(x') - F(x)$ (additivity). This area is greater than that of the rectangle of base $x' - x$ and altitude x^2, and less

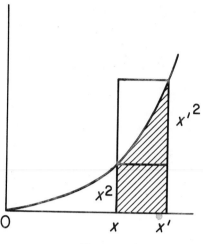

Fig. 3-1

than the area of the rectangle of base $x' - x$ and altitude x'^2 (additivity and positivity). Hence,

$$(x' - x)x^2 < F(x') - F(x) < (x' - x)x'^2. \tag{1}$$

This must be true for all $0 \leqslant x < x'$.

It is very easy to find a function F such that the double inequality (1) is satisfied for all $0 \leqslant x < x'$. It is clear that $F(x)$ is less than half the area of the rectangle of base x and altitude x^2, so that $F(x) = x^3/3$ [and $F(x') = x'^3/3$] is a good guess. In fact,

$$\frac{x'^3}{3} - \frac{x^3}{3} = (x' - x)\left(\frac{x^2 + xx' + x'^2}{3}\right)$$

is less than $(x' - x)x'^2$ and greater than $(x' - x)x^2$.

If desired, one can start with the easily derived inequality

$$(x' - x)3x^2 < x'^3 - x^3 < (x' - x)3x'^2$$

and divide by 3.

Of course, $F(x) = x^3/3$ is the correct solution. To justify it we must show that if there exists an area function F for which $F(0) = 0$ and

$$(x' - x)x^2 < F(x') - F(x) < (x' - x)x'^2$$

for all $0 \leqslant x < x'$, then this function is unique. We need not prove the *existence* of such a function, since, let us say, a bird in the hand is known to exist.

The essence of the method is to note that for a function f which increases on an interval $[a, b]$, an area function $F(x)$ must satisfy the double inequality

$$(x' - x)f(x) < F(x') - F(x) < (x' - x)f(x') \qquad (2)$$

for all $x < x'$ on the interval. For elementary functions, F can be found easily without dividing by $x' - x$ and passing to the limit as $x' \to x$, as is customary. The exhibition of such a function F makes it unnecessary to prove its existence. If $F(a) = 0$, which is easy to arrange, the theorem to be proved in the next section shows that $F(x)$ is the only possible answer for the required area above $[a, x]$.

Since we can treat decreasing functions by reversing the inequality signs in (2), this simple method is sufficient to handle elementary functions which are piecewise monotone.

3. THE UNIQUENESS PROOF

Theorem 1. Let f be a non-negative strictly increasing function on the interval $a \leqslant x \leqslant b$. Let $F(x)$ be the area below the graph of $y = f(x)$ and above the interval $[a, x]$. If $F(a) = 0$ and

$$(x' - x)f(x) < F(x') - F(x) < (x' - x)f(x') \qquad (2)$$

for all $a \leqslant x < x' \leqslant b$, F is uniquely defined.

PROOF: Assume that there exists a different function $\bar{F}$ satisfying (2) with $\bar{F}(a) = 0$ so that for some c $(a < c \leqslant b)$, $\bar{F}(c) \neq F(c)$.

Let $x_k = a + [k(c - a)/n]$, n being any positive integer and $k = 0, 1, 2, \ldots, n$.
Then

$$\frac{c - a}{n} f(x_{k-1}) < F(x_k) - F(x_{k-1}) < \frac{c - a}{n} f(x_k) \qquad (k = 1, 2, \ldots, n).$$

Summing from $k = 1$ to $k = n$,

$$\frac{c - a}{n} \sum_0^{n-1} f(x_k) < F(c) < \frac{c - a}{n} \sum_1^n f(x_k).$$

Similarly,

$$\frac{c - a}{n} \sum_0^{n-1} f(x_k) < \bar{F}(c) < \frac{c - a}{n} \sum_1^n f(x_k).$$

Hence

$$| \bar{F}(c) - F(c)| < \frac{(c - a)}{n} [f(c) - f(a)]$$

and

$$n < \frac{(c - a)[f(c) - f(a)]}{|\bar{F}(c) - F(c)|}.$$

for all positive integers n.

Since the Archimedean axiom assures us that there exists a positive integers n for which

$$n| \bar{F}(c) - F(c)| > (c - a)[f(c) - f(a)],$$

the assumption that $\bar{F}(c) \neq F(c)$ leads to a contradiction and must be rejected.

The proof is easily modified to treat decreasing functions where the inequality signs in (2) are reversed.

It will be observed that this proof does not require that f be continuous.* It therefore appears that no use has been made of the limit concept. Nor has the Cantor continuity postulate for the reals been used.

---

* I am indebted to Professor Robert H. Breusch for suggesting an improvement of a previous proof which did assume the continuity of f. See also Apostol, *Calculus*, vol. I, pp. 7–8.

4. AREAS UNDER POLYNOMIAL GRAPHS

The double inequality (2) is easily solved if $f(x) = cx^n$, $c > 0$, and n a positive integer. Since

$$x'^{\,n+1} - x^{n+1} = (x' - x)(x^n + x^{n-1}x' + \cdots + x'^{\,n})$$

is between $(x' - x)(n + 1)x^n$ and $(x' - x)(n + 1)x'^{\,n}$, we readily find $F(x) = cx^{n+1}/(n + 1)$. Of course, $F(0) = 0$.

To handle polynomial functions, we need two simple theorems.

Theorem 2. If f and g are non-negative strictly increasing functions on $x \geqslant 0$ and F and G are their respective area functions, $F + G$ is the area function for $f + g$.

PROOF: We add

$$(x' - x)f(x) < F(x') - F(x) < (x' - x)f(x')$$

and

$$(x' - x)\,g(x) < G(x') - G(x) < (x' - x)\,g(x')$$

and obtain

$$(x' - x)[f(x) + g(x)] < [F(x') + G(x')]$$
$$- [F(x) + G(x)] < (x' - x)[f(x') + g(x')].$$

Note that $(F + G)(0) = F(0) + G(0) = 0$.

Repeated use of this theorem gives the areas under polynomial graphs over any interval $[x, x']$, $x \geqslant 0$, provided that all the coefficients are positive.

For polynomials some of whose coefficients are negative, we may write the polynomial function as the difference of two increasing polynomial functions, p and q. ($f = p - q$.) We assume that we are dealing with an interval for which $p(x) > q(x)$. The graph of $f(x)$ consists of a finite number of pieces over which f increases or decreases. For definiteness, assume that f increases on the interval $[a, b]$.

Theorem 3.   *Let p and q be non-negative strictly increasing functions on $[a, b]$ and let P and Q be the corresponding area functions. Then if $f = p - q$ is positive and increasing (decreasing) on $[a, b]$, $F = P - Q$ is the area function for f.*

INTUITIVE PROOF: Let $a \leqslant x < u < x' \leqslant b$. Since $p - q$ increases,

$$p(u) - q(u) > p(x) - q(x).$$

Hence,

$$p(u) - p(x) > q(u) - q(x).$$

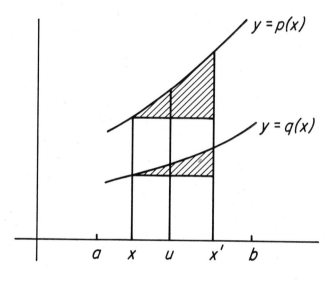

FIG. 3-2

Comparing the shaded areas in Figure 3-2, using the four properties of area,

$$P(x') - P(x) - (x' - x)p(x) > Q(x') - Q(x) - (x' - x)q(x).$$

Hence

$$[P(x') - Q(x')] - [P(x) - Q(x)] > (x' - x)[p(x) - q(x)],$$

that is,

$$F(x') - F(x) > (x' - x)f(x).$$

Similarly from

$$p(u) - q(u) < p(x') - q(x'),$$

we find that

$$F(x') - F(x) < (x' - x)f(x').$$

Since $F(0) = P(0) - Q(0)$, $F = P - Q$ is the required area function.

The reader may wish to make this proof rigorously analytic by substituting algebraic arguments for references to the figure, and then to compare his proof with that of the writer in the *American Mathematical Monthly*, vol. 73, pp. 477–483, May, 1966.

5. AREAS FOR OTHER FUNCTIONS

Our method for finding areas is not restricted to polynomial functions. It applies to almost all the functions customarily studied in a first course in calculus by virtue of the fact that these functions are piecewise monotone.

For example, with $F(x) = \sin x$ on $[0, \pi/2]$ we obtain

$$\sin x' - \sin x = 2 \sin\left(\frac{x' - x}{2}\right)\cos\left(\frac{x + x'}{2}\right)$$

$$< (x' - x)\cos x.$$

Also,

$$\sin x' - \sin x = 2 \tan\left(\frac{x' - x}{2}\right) \cdot \cos\left(\frac{x' - x}{2}\right) \cdot \cos\left(\frac{x + x'}{2}\right)$$

$$= \tan\left(\frac{x' - x}{2}\right) \cdot (\cos x + \cos x')$$

$$> (x' - x) \cos x'.$$

Thus, sin is the area function for cos.

Next consider the area $F(x)$ below the graph of $y = 1/x$ and above the interval $[1, x]$. We require (Figure 3-3) that

$$\frac{x' - x}{x'} < F(x') - F(x) < \frac{x' - x}{x}.$$

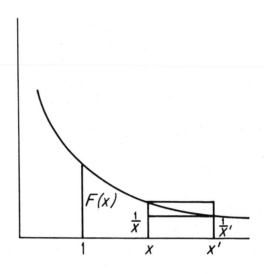

$$F(x)$$
$$\frac{1}{x}$$
$$\frac{1}{x'}$$

FIG. 3-3

Replace x by ax and x' by ax' $(a > 0)$. Then

$$\frac{x' - x}{x'} < F(ax') - F(ax) < \frac{x' - x}{x}.$$

By the uniqueness theorem, since $F(ax) - F(a)$, like $F(x)$, vanishes at $x = 1$,

$$F(ax) - F(a) = F(x)$$

and

$$F(ax) = F(a) + F(x).$$

Thus, if F exists, it must be a logarithmic function. (To establish the existence of F requires the use of limits. However, the argument is a very simple and familiar one.)

Our two examples illustrate the power of the double inequality (2). It will be found that all of the usual calculus results for elementary functions can be derived with great ease.

6. VOLUMES

Let a solid be cut by a plane perpendicular to the x-axis at abscissa $x(\geqslant 0)$. Let its cross-sectional area $S(x)$ increase with x. If $F(x)$ is the volume between the planes at 0 and x, and $F(x')$ the volume between the planes at 0 and x', we have the double inequality

$$(x' - x)\, S(x) < F(x') - F(x) < (x' - x)\, S(x'), \qquad x' > x. \quad (3)$$

For example, if the cross section is a square of area x^2, then

$$(x' - x)x^2 < F(x') - F(x) < (x' - x)x'^{\,2}. \quad (4)$$

This is the same inequality (1) that arose in connection with the area below the parabola. But in (4), $F(x)$ is the volume of a square pyramid. Hence $F(x) = \frac{1}{3}x^2 x = x^3/3$ and $F(x') = x'^{\,3}/3$. Therefore, (1) could have been solved by referring to the square pyramid. The area under a parabola is just as elementary as the volume of a pyramid! This does not seem to have been noticed. Archimedes could have saved himself some trouble.

The volumes of solids of revolution can be found from (3) if we assume, as is usual in calculus courses, that the area of a circle is known. If the radius $r = f(x)$ at distance x decreases, then

$$(x' - x)\, \pi f^2(x) > F(x') - F(x) > (x' - x)\, \pi f^2(x').$$

For example, for a hemisphere of radius a and center at the origin, $f^2(x) = a^2 - x^2$. Since the volume functions for a^2 and x^2 are $a^2 x$ and $x^3/3$, respectively, $F(x)$ for $\pi(a^2 - x^2)$ is $\pi(a^2 x - (x^3/3))$. The required volume is $F(a) = 2\pi a^3/3$.

It should be clear that problems which involve the distance for a given velocity, the work against a variable force, and the like, are equally easy to set up and solve by a simple use of inequalities.

7. REMARKS

It is immediately clear that the ordinate function f is the derivative of what we have called the area function F. The method of this paper therefore gives a way of finding derivatives without the use of a limit process.

When f is increasing, the graph of $y = F(x)$ is convex and the tangent is characterized by the fact that the curve lies above it except at one point. In fact, for $x > a$,

$$(x - a)f(a) < F(x) - F(a),$$

that is,

$$F(x) > F(a) + f(a)(x - a).$$

For $x < a$,

$$F(a) - F(x) < (a - x)f(a)$$

and

$$F(x) > F(a) + f(a)(x - a).$$

Thus $F(x)$ is above $y = F(a) + f(a)(x - a)$ for all $x \neq a$ on the interval over which f increases.

Similarly, if f decreases, $F(x) < F(a) + f(a)(x - a)$ for $x \neq a$.

The fact is that our method enables one to develop what might be called a "calculus in the large" which closely parallels the results of elementary calculus.

It is frequently emphasized that greater attention should be given to the study of inequalities. However, the applications customarily given do not convince most students of their importance. The fact that results traditionally found by calculus methods can be obtained so easily from the algebra of inequalities immediately opens up significant applications of this algebra. Moreover, it enables the student to handle these applications without the subtleties of limit theory.

4

Area and Integration

HANS SAGAN

NORTH CAROLINA STATE UNIVERSITY

Hans Sagan, Professor of Mathematics at North Carolina State University, was born in Vienna and received his Doctor's Degree at the University there in 1950. Before assuming his present position, he taught at the Austrian Technical University, Montana State University, and the University of Idaho. In 1964 he was visiting professor at the University of Technology in Munich. He is an Associate Editor of *The Mathematics Magazine*, and has lectured widely in connection with programs for strengthening teaching at all levels. His research interests are reflected in his books *Die Laplace Transformation und Ihre Anwendung* (with P. Funk and F. Selig), and *Boundary and Eigenvalue Problems in Mathematical Physics*. He is also author of *Integral and Differential Calculus—an Intuitive Approach*.

In the following lecture Professor Sagan discusses area and integration in a way that leads naturally to the Lebesgue integral which has revolutionized integration theory in the twentieth century.

AREA AND INTEGRATION

Hans Sagan

1. RIEMANN INTEGRAL

Let us consider the function

$$f(x) = 0 \text{ for } x = 0$$
$$= 1 \text{ for } 1/2 < x \leqslant 1$$
$$= 0 \text{ for } 1/3 < x \leqslant 1/2$$
$$= 1 \text{ for } 1/4 < x \leqslant 1/3$$
$$= 0 \text{ for } 1/5 < x \leqslant 1/4$$
$$\vdots$$
$$\left.\begin{array}{l} = 0 \\ = 1 \end{array}\right\} \text{ for } \frac{1}{n} < x \leqslant \frac{1}{n-1} \quad \text{if } \begin{cases} n \text{ is odd} \\ n \text{ is even} \end{cases}$$
$$\vdots$$

(see Figure 4-1) which is defined on the closed interval $0 \leqslant x \leqslant 1$. Even though this function has infinitely many discontinuities in the interval $0 \leqslant x \leqslant 1$, it seems reasonable to speak of an area of the region "under the curve" which is represented by $f(x)$. Although this region consists of infinitely many rectangles, these rectangles are nonoverlapping and they are all enclosed in a square of area 1.

Customarily, the Riemann integral is utilized to find areas

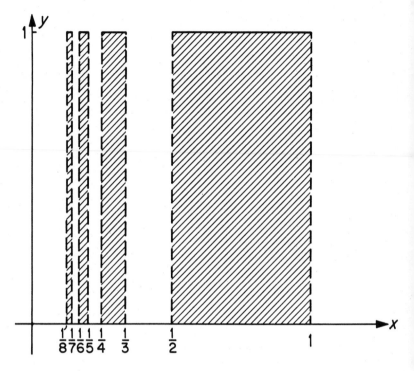

Fig. 4-1

under curves and we will see in the sequel that the combined area of all these infinitely many rectangles can indeed be found by Riemann integration.

In order to show that the Riemann integral $\int_0^1 f(x) \, dx$ exists, we will demonstrate that for any $\varepsilon > 0$, no matter how small, there exists a subdivision σ_μ of the interval $[0, 1]$ so that

$$\bar{S}_\mu - \underline{S}_\mu < \varepsilon,$$

where $\bar{S}_\mu$ is the upper sum and $\underline{S}_\mu$ is the lower sum corresponding to the subdivision σ_μ. (See Ref. [1].)

Let us choose an $\varepsilon > 0$ and subsequently an integer n so that

$$\frac{2}{n} < \varepsilon. \tag{1}$$

Next, we consider a subdivision

$$\sigma_\mu : 0 = x_0 < x_1 < x_2 < \cdots < x_\mu = 1$$

so that

$$|\Delta x| = \max_{(k)} |x_{k+1} - x_k| < \frac{1}{2n^2}. \tag{2}$$

In order to find an estimate of the difference of upper and lower sum, let us first evaluate the sum of the areas of all the shaded rectangles (Figure 4-1) between $x = 1/n$ and $x = 1$. We obtain

$$A_n = 1 - \frac{1}{2} + \frac{1}{3} - \frac{1}{4} + \frac{1}{5} - \cdots + \begin{cases} \dfrac{1}{n-1} - \dfrac{1}{n} \text{ if } n \text{ is even} \\[2ex] \dfrac{1}{n-2} - \dfrac{1}{n-1} \text{ if } n \text{ is odd.} \end{cases} \tag{3}$$

If a subinterval $\Delta x_k = [x_{k-1}, x_k]$ of our subdivision σ_μ contains one of the points $1/k$ ($k = 1, 2, 3, \ldots, n$), then we clearly have

$$\min_{\Delta x_k} f(x) = 0.$$

Hence, if we subtract from A_n at every point of discontinuity the horizontally striped rectangles (see Figure 4-2) and ignore the portion between $x = 0$ and $x = 1/n$ entirely, then we obtain certainly a number that is smaller than the lower sum $\underline{S}_\mu$ that belongs to the subdivision σ_μ:

$$\underline{S}_\mu \geqslant A_n - |\Delta x|(n-1). \tag{4}$$

If Δx_k contains one of the points $x = 1/k$ and since then

$$\max_{\Delta x_k} f(x) = 1,$$

we obtain a number that is larger than the upper sum $\bar{S}_\mu$ if we add to A_n all the vertically striped rectangles (Figure 4-2) and also add the area of a rectangle of height 1 and width $1/n$ to dominate the contribution to the upper sum that comes from that portion of our function $f(x)$ that lies in $0 \leqslant x \leqslant 1/n$:

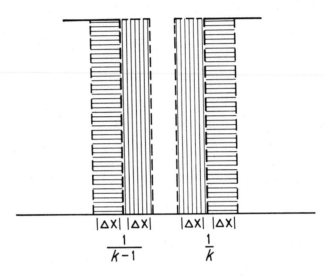

FIG. 4-2

$$\bar{S}_\mu \leqslant A_n + |\Delta x|(n-1) + \frac{1}{n}. \tag{5}$$

Since $\underline{S}_\mu \leqslant \bar{S}_\mu$ for any subdivision σ_μ, we may combine the two inequalities (4) and (5) and obtain

$$A_n - |\Delta x|(n-1) \leqslant \underline{S}_\mu \leqslant \bar{S}_\mu \leqslant A_n + |\Delta x|(n+1) + \frac{1}{n}. \tag{6}$$

Therefore,

$$\bar{S}_\mu - \underline{S}_\mu \leqslant A_n + |\Delta x|(n-1) + \frac{1}{n} - \underline{S}_\mu$$

$$\leqslant A_n + |\Delta x|(n-1) + \frac{1}{n} - A_n + |\Delta x|(n-1)$$

$$= 2|\Delta x|(n-1) + \frac{1}{n}.$$

By (2), $|\Delta x| < \dfrac{1}{2n^2}$ and we obtain

$$\bar{S}_\mu - \underline{S}_\mu < \frac{n-1}{n^2} + \frac{1}{n} = \frac{2}{n} - \frac{1}{n^2} < \frac{2}{n}$$

and from (1)

$$\bar{S}_\mu - \underline{S}_\mu < \varepsilon.$$

Thus it follows that $\int_0^1 f(x)\, dx$ exists.

Since

$$\log(1+h) = h - \frac{h^2}{2} + \frac{h^3}{3} - \cdots$$

converges for $-1 < h \leqslant 1$ (see Ref. [2]), we have

$$\lim_{n\to\infty} A_n = \log 2$$

and it is easy to see that

$$\log 2 = \text{l.u.b. } \underline{S}_\mu = \text{g.l.b. } \bar{S}_\mu$$

for all possible subdivisions σ_μ. Hence,

$$\int_0^1 f(x)\, dx = \log 2$$

(see Ref. [3]).

2. LEBESGUE INTEGRAL

Encouraged by this spectacular success in a bold venture, we consider now another function which also "jumps" infinitely many times from the 0-level to the 1-level. ("jump" is used throughout this paper in the naive sense and *not* equivocally with "jump-discontinuity.") Take

$$g(x) = \begin{cases} 1 \text{ for all irrational values of } x \text{ in } [0, 1] \\ 0 \text{ for all rational values of } x \text{ in } [0, 1]. \end{cases}$$

Since there are only countably many rational numbers and since $g(x)$ "jumps" at every rational point from the 1-level to the 0-level and back again, it appears that $g(x)$ has only countably many "jumps." (The union of two sets of countably many elements each again contains only countably many elements.)

Since the cardinality of all irrational numbers in [0, 1] is that of the continuum c, and since $c > \aleph_0$, the cardinality of a set of countably many elements, we see that our function $g(x)$ has really relatively few "holes" on the 1-level and we may depict it graphically as in Figure 4-3 if we agree that the stroke-dotted line

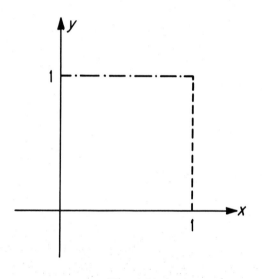

Fig. 4-3

has holes vertically above all rational abscissas.

Though the function $g(x)$ "jumps" just as often (or strictly speaking "twice" as often—see the parenthetical remark above—as the function $f(x)$) ($f(x)$ jumps at the points 0, 1/2, 1/3, 1/4, ..., a set of cardinality $\aleph_0$) and though $g(x)$ looks so much better than $f(x)$, a very simple argument will reveal that $g(x)$ is *not* Riemann integrable.

Take any subdivision $\sigma_\mu : 0 = x_0 < x_1 < x_2 < \cdots < x_\mu = 1$. Every one of the thus created subintervals $[x_{k-1}, x_k]$ will contain rational as well as irrational points. Hence

$$\min_{\Delta x_k} g(x) = g(\underline{\xi}_k) = 0,$$

and consequently

$$\underline{S}_\mu = \sum_{k=1}^{n} g(\underline{\xi}_k)\Delta x_k = 0.$$

By the same token, the value of any upper sum will be 1, since

$$\max_{\Delta x_k} g(x) = g(\bar{\xi}_k) = 1,$$

and consequently

$$\bar{S}_\mu = \sum_{k=1}^{n} g(\bar{\xi}_k)\Delta x_k = 1.$$

Therefore, $\int_0^1 g(x) \, dx$ does *not* exist in the Riemann sense.

Of course, we have our suspicions of why the Riemann integral does not exist in the latter case. Let us back up a little and re-examine $f(x)$. The function $f(x)$ has *discontinuities* on a set of points of cardinality $\aleph_0$ (the points $0, 1/2, 1/3, 1/4, \ldots$). The elements of any set of cardinality $\aleph_0$ can be enumerated in some order $r_1, r_2, r_3, \ldots$ and each point r_k of this set can be enclosed in an open interval of length $\varepsilon/2^k$, where ε may be chosen arbitrarily small. Thus, the total length of the union of all these intervals will be less than

$$\frac{\varepsilon}{2} + \frac{\varepsilon}{4} + \frac{\varepsilon}{8} + \cdots = \frac{\varepsilon}{2}\left(1 + \frac{1}{2} + \frac{1}{4} + \cdots\right) = \varepsilon,$$

i.e., can be made arbitrarily small. We say in such a case that $f(x)$ is continuous almost everywhere. ("Almost everywhere" has the precise meaning: everywhere except on a set of points that can be enclosed on a collection of open intervals the total length of the union of which can be made arbitrarily small.)

On the other hand, $g(x)$ is discontinuous *everywhere* even though it only "jumps" at the points of a set of cardinality $\aleph_0$. This can be seen as follows:

Let r be a rational point on the interval $[0, 1]$. Then $g(r) = 0$ and

$$|g(r) - g(x)| = |g(x)| = 0 \text{ or } 1,$$

depending on whether x is rational or irrational, no matter how close x is chosen to r. Thus, $g(x)$ is discontinuous at all rational points. Now, let x be irrational. Then

$$|g(x) - g(x')| = |1 - g(x')| = 1 \text{ or } 0,$$

depending on whether x' is rational or irrational and regardless of how close x and x' are. Hence, $g(x)$ is also discontinuous at all irrational points.

(These results on $f(x)$ and $g(x)$ illustrate the necessary and sufficient condition for the Riemann integrability of bounded functions, namely that the function has to be continuous almost everywhere. See Ref. [4].)

Still, speaking naively, $g(x)$ does not "jump" any more often than $f(x)$ does, as pointed out already, and some modification of the concept of the integral might enable us to integrate functions of the type $g(x)$ as well. To study such a possibility, let us re-examine the function $f(x)$ and its integral, disregarding for the moment all that hocus pocus with upper and lower sums. All we really did in the end when it came to the evaluation of $\int_0^1 f(x)\, dx$ was take the limit of A_n as $n \to \infty$, and we saw that

$$\lim_{n \to \infty} A_n = \int_0^1 f(x)\, dx = \log 2.$$

Now, what is A_n? It is the area under the "curve" that is represented by the function

$$f_n(x) = 1 \text{ for } 1/2 < x \leqslant 1$$
$$= 0 \text{ for } 1/3 < x \leqslant 1/2$$
$$\vdots$$
$$\left.\begin{array}{l} = 0 \\ = 1 \end{array}\right\} \text{ for } \frac{1}{n} < x \leqslant \frac{1}{n-1} \text{ if } \begin{cases} n \text{ is odd} \\ n \text{ is even} \end{cases}$$
$$= 0 \text{ for } 0 \leqslant x \leqslant \frac{1}{n},$$

which has finitely many discontinuities and has a constant value between two consecutive discontinuities. Such a function is called a stepfunction.

We can see that

$$\lim_{n \to \infty} f_n(x) = f(x),$$

and it turned out that

$$\int_0^1 f(x)\, dx = \lim_{n \to \infty} \int_0^1 f_n(x)\, dx = \lim_{n \to \infty} A_n = \log 2.$$

Let us now try to apply the same process to the function $g(x)$. First, we represent the function $g(x)$ as the limit of a sequence of suitably chosen stepfunctions, each of which has finitely many discontinuities only. Let $r_1, r_2, r_3, \ldots$ be some enumeration of the rational numbers in the interval $[0, 1]$. We define now

$$g_1(x) = \begin{cases} 0 \text{ at } x = r_1 \\ 1 \text{ on the point set } [0, 1] - \{r_1\}. \end{cases}$$

$$g_2(x) = \begin{cases} 0 \text{ on the point set } \{r_1, r_2\} \\ 1 \text{ on the point set } [0, 1] - \{r_1, r_2\}. \end{cases}$$

$$\vdots$$

$$g_n(x) = \begin{cases} 0 \text{ on the point set } \{r_1, r_2, \ldots, r_n\} \\ 1 \text{ on the point set } [0, 1] - \{r_1, r_2, \ldots, r_n\}, \end{cases}$$

etc., where $[0, 1]$ denotes the closed interval from 0 to 1 and where braces denote discrete point sets. The function $g_5(x)$ is depicted in Figure 4-4.

Obviously

$$\lim_{n \to \infty} g_n(x) = g(x).$$

Since

$$\int_0^1 g_n(x)\, dx = 1 \qquad \text{for all } n,$$

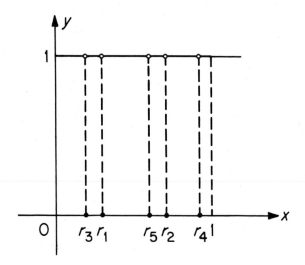

FIG. 4-4

we have

$$\lim_{n \to \infty} \int_0^1 g_n(x)\, dx = 1$$

and we simply *define*

$$\int_0^1 g(x)\, dx = \lim_{n \to \infty} \int_0^1 g_n(x)\, dx = 1,$$

where the integral on the left is definitely *not* a Riemann integral. This is a new concept of an integral which was first proposed by Henri Lebesgue in 1902 and is called in his honor the *Lebesgue integral*.

We see that, in the case of $f(x)$, the Riemann integral and the Lebesgue integral both exist and yield the same value. In the case of $g(x)$, the Riemann integral does not exist, but the Lebesgue integral does.

In general, one can arrive at the Lebesgue integral as follows (see Ref. [5]): If $I_1, I_2, I_3, \ldots$ are intervals of finite length $|I_k|$ that are all contained in a finite or infinite interval (a, b) and do not overlap, then

$$g_n(x) = \begin{cases} c_{n_j} \text{ in } I_{n_j}, & j = 1, 2, \ldots, k_n \\ 0 \text{ in } (a, b) - U_1^{n_k} I_{n_j} \end{cases}$$

(c_k constants) is called a stepfunction.

If $\{g_n(x)\}$ is a nondecreasing (nonincreasing) sequence of stepfunctions—the sequence $\{f_n(x)\}$ of our first example is a nondecreasing sequence and the sequence $\{g_n(x)\}$ of our second example is nonincreasing—that converges to a function $g(x)$ almost everywhere, and if $|\int_a^b g_n(x)\,dx| \leqslant M$ for all n, then the Lebesgue integral of $g(x)$ is defined as

$$\int_a^b g(x)\,dx = \lim_{n \to \infty} \int_a^b g_n(x)\,dx,$$

where

$$\int_a^b g_n(x)\,dx = \sum_{j=1}^{k_n} c_{n_j} |I_{n_j}|.$$

One can show that this integral is independent of the selected sequence $\{g_n(x)\}$ as long as the limit of the sequence is almost everywhere equal to $g(x)$, the sequence is nondecreasing (nonincreasing), and the (Riemann) integrals over all the $g_n(x)$ are bounded by a constant independent of n.

One can then extend the definition of the Lebesgue integral to the class of functions that can be written as the difference of two functions of the type as arrived at by the process outlined above. Further, if one now considers nonincreasing (nondecreasing) sequences of functions of this latter type which converge to a certain function almost everywhere and are such that the (Lebesgue) integral over each element of the sequence is uniformly bounded, one can show that one does *not* arrive at a new class of functions, but that these functions are again of the type that can be written as the difference of two functions defined by the limit of sequences of stepfunctions as outlined above.

REFERENCES

[1] Angus E. Taylor, *Advanced Calculus*, Ginn and Company, 1955, p. 507.
[2] *Op. cit.*, p. 542.
[3] *Op. cit.*, p. 506.
[4] *Op. cit.*, p. 512.
[5] Fr. Riesz and Bela Sz-Nagy, *Functional Analysis*, F. Ungar, 1955, pp. 29–38.

5

Geometrical Applications of Integral Calculus

HEINRICH W. GUGGENHEIMER

POLYTECHNIC INSTITUTE OF BROOKLYN

After receiving his Sc.D. from the Swiss Federal Institute of Technology in Zurich in 1950, Professor Heinrich W. Guggenheimer taught at Hebrew University and Bar-Ilan University in Israel, Washington State University, and the University of Minnesota before assuming his present position as Professor of Mathematics at the Polytechnic Institute of Brooklyn. His main research interests are in differential geometry, algebraic topology, and the foundations of geometry. He was an invited speaker at the International Colloquia on differential geometry in 1953, on the foundations of geometry in 1959, on algebraic geometry in 1965, and on differential geometry in 1967. He is a member of the Board of Editors of *Dialectica*, an international review of the philosophy of knowledge. He is the author of modern textbooks on differential geometry and elementary geometry.

Professor Guggenheimer's lecture presents a number of elementary, but modern and interesting applications of integral calculus which for the student may be a welcome change from computing areas, volumes, moments, and arc lengths.

GEOMETRICAL APPLICATIONS OF
INTEGRAL CALCULUS

Heinrich W. Guggenheimer

Most calculus texts contain fairly interesting applications of differential calculus, but the applications of integral calculus usually reduce to the computation of areas, volumes, moments, and arc lengths. Here we explain some modern, but elementary, applications of integral calculus to the study of properties of smooth, closed, convex curves (ovals).

1. INTRODUCTION

An arbitrary, nonzero, continuous function is always the radius of curvature of some arc without inflection points. But it is clear that a function must have quite special properties if it is to define the radius of curvature of an oval. We may consider the radius of curvature as a function of the point on the oval. As such it is periodic, and has at least one maximum and one minimum. We shall show that, in fact, the radius of curvature of an oval must have at least two maxima and two minima. This means, e.g., that a function like $a + b \cos \phi (0 \leqslant \phi \leqslant 2\pi)$ cannot be the radius of curvature of an oval in polar coordinates. In addition, the maxima and minima cannot be too close in the sense that at least two

75

maxima are not smaller, and two minima not bigger than the mean value of the radius of curvature on the oval. Similar properties (at least four extrema evenly divided about the mean) are exhibited by a number of other functions connected with ovals, in particular the distances of the points of the oval from the area centroid and certain other centroids. That these theorems are not trivial is seen from the fact that for the circle the center is the only point for which the distance to the points on the circumference does not have a unique maximum and a unique minimum.

Another set of results is represented by theorems like the following: " On every oval there exist at least three pairs of points at which the tangents are parallel and the radii of curvature are equal," or " At least three chords of an oval are bisected at its area centroid." The last statement, again, characterizes its center with respect to the circle.

Some historical remarks and references are given at the end of this paper. They refer to the simple analytical approach followed here. There exists a vast literature connected with the (projective) geometrical side of these "four" and "three" theorems.

We have to start with some developments of analytical geometry which are needed for the study of ovals.

The treatment of differentiable curves in terms of polar coordinates

$$r = r(\phi)$$

is assumed to be known from the textbooks. An alternative treatment uses the tangent angle θ as main parameter (Figure 5-1). If the curve is given in parametric form

$$x = x(t) \qquad y = y(t),$$

the tangent angle can be computed from

$$\tan \theta = \frac{dy}{dx}. \tag{1}$$

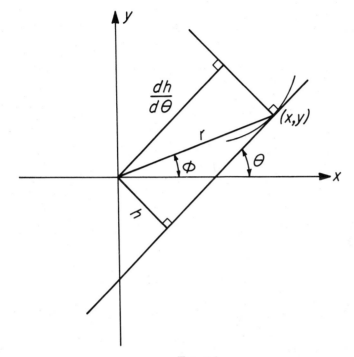

FIG. 5-1

The arc length is defined as an integral of $ds = (dx^2 + dy^2)^{1/2}$. Hence

$$\cos \theta = \frac{dx}{ds}, \qquad \sin \theta = \frac{dy}{ds}. \tag{2}$$

The equation of the tangent line to the curve at any point $(x(t),\ y(t))$ can be written as

$$X \sin \theta - Y \cos \theta = h(\theta), \tag{3}$$

where

$$h(\theta) = x(t) \sin \theta(t) - y(t) \cos \theta(t),$$

the *support function* of the arc for the angle θ, is the distance from the origin of the tangent line, and X, Y are the running coordinates on the line.

Equation (3) is the equation of a family of straight lines, depending on the parameter θ, whose envelope is the given curve. Computing this envelope, we obtain the parametric representation of the curve

$$x(\theta) = h(\theta) \sin \theta + \frac{dh}{d\theta} \cos \theta,$$

$$y(\theta) = -h(\theta) \cos \theta + \frac{dh}{d\theta} \sin \theta. \tag{4}$$

The curvature radius is defined by

$$\rho = \frac{ds}{d\theta}. \tag{5}$$

From (4) one obtains

$$\frac{dx}{d\theta} = [h(\theta) + h''(\theta)] \cos \theta, \qquad \frac{dy}{d\theta} = [h(\theta) + h''(\theta)] \sin \theta.$$

A comparison with (2) and (5) shows that

$$\rho = h(\theta) + h''(\theta). \tag{6}$$

From (4) one also has

$$r^2(\theta) = h^2(\theta) + h'^2(\theta), \tag{7}$$

hence

$$\frac{d(r^2)}{d\theta} = 2\,\rho(\theta)h'(\theta). \tag{8}$$

For the whole theory we have to suppose that $\rho(\theta)$ is continuous and of constant sign. For these *convex arcs* it is possible to choose the orientation of the curve in order to have $\rho > 0$. A convex arc is *simple closed* if for each value θ between 0 and 2π there exists exactly one point on the curve for which θ is the tangent angle, and if the parametric representation

$$x = x(\theta), \qquad y = y(\theta)$$

is by periodic functions of period 2π:

$$x(\theta) = x(\theta + 2\pi), \qquad y(\theta) = y(\theta + 2\pi). \tag{9}$$

A straight line can intersect a simple closed, convex curve (an *oval*) in at most two points; otherwise θ could not be univalent on the oval. It follows from (9) that $h(\theta)$ also is periodic:

$$h(\theta) = h(\theta + 2\pi).$$

By (2) and (5)

$$x(\theta) = x(0) + \int_0^\theta \rho(\vartheta) \cos \vartheta \, d\vartheta ,$$

$$y(\theta) = y(0) + \int_0^\theta \rho(\vartheta) \sin \vartheta \, d\vartheta .$$

(10)

Hence for an oval

$$\int_0^{2\pi} \rho(\theta) \cos \theta \, d\theta = \int_0^{2\pi} \rho(\theta) \sin \theta \, d\theta = 0. \tag{11}$$

Integration by parts is particularly simple if effected over an oval. Let $u(\theta)$, $v(\theta)$ be two functions defined on our curve; then

$$u(0) = u(2\pi), \qquad v(0) = v(2\pi).$$

Hence

$$\int_0^{2\pi} u(\theta) \, dv(\theta) = uv \Big|_0^{2\pi} - \int_0^{2\pi} v(\theta) \, du(\theta) = - \int_0^{2\pi} v(\theta) \, du(\theta). \tag{12}$$

In particular,

$$\int_0^{2\pi} dv(\theta) = 0. \tag{13}$$

For the total length of the curve we obtain

$$L = \int_0^{2\pi} ds(\theta) = \int_0^{2\pi} [h(\theta) + h''(\theta)] \, d\theta.$$

But $h(\theta)$ is periodic and so are its derivatives, i.e., by (13),

$$\int_0^{2\pi} h''(\theta) \, d\theta = \int_0^{2\pi} dh'(\theta) = 0,$$

or

$$L = \int_0^{2\pi} h(\theta) \, d\theta. \tag{14}$$

The area enclosed by the oval can be computed from

$$A = \frac{1}{2} \int_0^{2\pi} \begin{vmatrix} x(\theta) & y(\theta) \\ dx(\theta) & dy(\theta) \end{vmatrix} = \frac{1}{2} \int_0^{2\pi} (h^2 - h'^2) \, d\theta, \tag{15}$$

hence, also, by (12),

$$A = \frac{1}{2} \int_0^{2\pi} h(\theta) \, ds \, (\theta). \tag{16}$$

The mean $\bar{f}$ of a periodic function $f(\theta)$ is defined by

$$\bar{f} = \frac{1}{2\pi} \int_0^{2\pi} f(\theta) \, d\theta. \tag{17}$$

We are also interested in certain centers of mass defined in integral calculus. The *mass centroid* corresponds to a constant density 1 in the interior of the oval. Its coordinates x_m, y_m are defined by

$$A x_m = \int_0^{2\pi} \int_0^{r(\phi)} x(r, \phi) r \, dr \, d\phi = \frac{1}{3} \int_0^{2\pi} r^3(\phi) \cos \phi \, d\phi.$$

$$A y_m = \int_0^{2\pi} \int_0^{r(\phi)} y(r, \phi) r \, dr \, d\phi = \frac{1}{3} \int_0^{2\pi} r^3(\phi) \sin \phi \, d\phi. \tag{18}$$

The *curvature centroid* (x_c, y_c) is the center of mass of density $1/\rho$ distributed on the oval,

$$2\pi x_c = \int_0^{2\pi} \frac{1}{\rho(\theta)} x(\theta) \, ds(\theta) = \int_0^{2\pi} x(\theta) \, d\theta,$$

$$2\pi y_c = \int_0^{2\pi} \frac{1}{\rho(\theta)} y(\theta) \, ds(\theta) = \int_0^{2\pi} y(\theta) \, d\theta. \tag{19}$$

Here $2\pi = \int_0^{2\pi} \dfrac{ds(\theta)}{\rho(\theta)}$ is the total mass. By (4),

$$2\pi x_c = \int_0^{2\pi} h \sin \theta \, d\theta + \int_0^{2\pi} h' \cos \theta \, d\theta = 2 \int_0^{2\pi} h \sin \theta \, d\theta,$$

$$2\pi y_c = -\int_0^{2\pi} h \cos \theta \, d\theta + \int_0^{2\pi} h' \sin \theta \, d\theta = -2 \int_0^{2\pi} h \cos \theta \, d\theta. \tag{20}$$

Finally, let us consider a mass distribution of density $\mu = [\rho(\theta)h^2(\theta)]^{-1}$. (This density does not refer to the oval alone, but it makes sense only if the origin of our system of coordinates is fixed.) Its center of mass (x^*, y^*) has coordinates

$$x^* \int_0^{2\pi} \mu \, ds = \int_0^{2\pi} \mu(\theta) x(\theta) \, ds(\theta) = \int_0^{2\pi} \left(\frac{1}{h} \sin \theta + \frac{h'}{h^2} \cos \theta \right) d\theta = 0,$$

(21)

$$y^* \int_0^{2\pi} \mu \, ds = \int_0^{2\pi} \mu(\theta) y(\theta) \, ds(\theta)$$

$$= \int_0^{2\pi} \left(-\frac{1}{h} \cos \theta + \frac{h'}{h^2} \sin \theta \right) d\theta = 0.$$

Any point P in the interior of the oval is the center of mass of the density μ on the oval if $h(\theta)$ is measured from P. In this case P is the origin $(0, 0)$, $h(\theta) > 0$, $\mu(\theta) > 0$, and, by the previous formulas, $(x^*, y^*) = (0, 0)$.

Finally, let $\alpha = \theta - \phi$ be the angle between radius vector and tangent at any point of the curve. It follows from Figure 5-1 that

$$\sin \alpha = \frac{h}{r} = \frac{r}{\sqrt{r^2 + (dr/d\phi)^2}}.$$

(22)

2. FOUR EXTREMA THEOREMS

In each of the following sections we shall prove a statement about integrals and then deduce from it some geometrical consequences.

Theorem 1. *Let $f(\theta), g(\theta)$ be two differentiable,[†] periodic functions of period 2π which satisfy*

$$\int_0^{2\pi} f(\theta) \sin \theta \, d\theta = \int_0^{2\pi} g(\theta) \sin \theta \, d\theta = 0,$$

$$\int_0^{2\pi} f(\theta) \cos \theta \, d\theta = \int_0^{2\pi} g(\theta) \cos \theta \, d\theta = 0,$$

---

† This hypothesis can be relaxed by using more advanced tools of analysis.

and suppose that $g(\theta) > 0$. Then the function $f(\theta)/g(\theta)$ has at least two maxima and two minima in $0 < \theta \leqslant 2\pi$.

By our hypothesis and definitions, the curve

$$x(\theta) = x(0) + \int_0^\theta g(\vartheta) \cos \vartheta \, d\vartheta, \qquad y(\theta) = y(0) + \int_0^\theta g(\vartheta) \sin \vartheta \, d\vartheta$$

is an oval C and $g(\theta)$ is its radius of curvature. From (12) and (13) we obtain through (2) and (5)

$$\int_0^{2\pi} d\,\frac{f(\theta)}{g(\theta)} = 0\,,$$

$$\int_0^{2\pi} x(\theta)\, d\,\frac{f(\theta)}{g(\theta)} = -\int_0^{2\pi} \frac{f(\theta)}{g(\theta)}\, dx(\theta) = -\int_0^{2\pi} f(\theta) \cos \theta \, d\theta = 0,$$

$$\int_0^{2\pi} y(\theta)\, d\,\frac{f(\theta)}{g(\theta)} = -\int_0^{2\pi} \frac{f(\theta)}{g(\theta)}\, dy(\theta) = -\int_0^{2\pi} f(\theta) \sin \theta \, d\theta = 0,$$

Hence, for any linear function $L(x,\,y) = ax + by + c$ (a, b, c constants)

$$\int_0^{2\pi} L[x(\theta),\, y(\theta)]\, d\,\frac{f(\theta)}{g(\theta)} = 0. \tag{23}$$

Now consider f/g as a function defined on the oval C. Since C is closed and bounded, by a standard theorem of calculus due to Weierstrass, f/g has at least one maximum and one minimum on C. So all we have to show is that it is impossible for f/g to have only one maximum and one minimum on C, i.e., in $0 \leqslant \theta \leqslant 2\pi$. In order to derive a contradiction, let us assume that there exists only one maximum, attained for $\theta = \theta_M$, and one minimum, attained for $\theta = \theta_m$. By choosing a new system of coordinates, we may assume that $0 = \theta_M < \theta_m < 2\pi$. Let $L(x,\,y) = ax + by + c = 0$ be the equation of the straight line connecting the points $[x(\theta_M),\, y(\theta_M)]$ and $[x(\theta_m),\, y(\theta_m)]$. Since the curve is intersected by the line at two points and $ds/d\theta > 0$, each one of the arcs

$$0 < \theta < \theta_m\,, \qquad \theta_m < \theta < 2\pi$$

is completely in one of the halfplanes defined by the line $L = 0$. We are still free to choose the sign of $L(x, y)$ and we do it by asking that

$$L(x, y) < 0, \qquad \text{for } 0 < \theta < \theta_m,$$

$$L(x, y) > 0, \qquad \text{for } \theta_m < \theta < 2\pi.$$

On the other hand, f/g decreases from 0 to θ_m, increases from θ to 2π,

$$\left(\frac{f(\theta)}{g(\theta)}\right)' \leqslant 0, \qquad \text{for } 0 < \theta < \theta_m,$$

$$\left(\frac{f(\theta)}{g(\theta)}\right)' \geqslant 0, \qquad \text{for } \theta_m < \theta < 2\pi,$$

and the equality cannot hold everywhere.
But this means that

$$\int_0^{2\pi} L[x(\theta), y(\theta)]\, d\,\frac{f(\theta)}{g(\theta)} = \int_0^{\theta m} L[x(\theta), y(\theta)] \left(\frac{f(\theta)}{g(\theta)}\right)' d\theta$$

$$+ \int_{\theta_m}^{2\pi} L[x(\theta), y(\theta)] \left(\frac{f(\theta)}{g(\theta)}\right)' d\theta > 0,$$

in contradiction to (23). So the line $L = 0$ cannot exist. ∎

Corollary 1.1. Let $\rho_1(\theta)$, $\rho_2(\theta)$ be the curvature radii of two ovals. Then $\rho_1(\theta)/\rho_2(\theta)$ has at least two maxima and two minima for $0 \leqslant \theta \leqslant 2\pi$.

In particular, $g(\theta) = 1$ is an admissible choice in Theorem 1.

Corollary 1.2. The radius of curvature of an oval has at least two relative maxima and two relative minima on the oval.

If $\rho_1 = \rho(\theta)$ is the curvature radius of an oval and γ a fixed angle, $\rho_2 = \rho(\theta + \gamma)$ is the curvature radius of an oval obtained from the first one by a rotation of angle γ about the origin. For differentiable $\rho(\theta)$, Corollary 1.1 shows that

$$\rho'(\theta)\, \rho(\theta + \gamma) - \rho(\theta)\, \rho'(\theta + \gamma) = 0 \qquad (24)$$

has at least four solutions for any constant γ. The function

$$\frac{\rho'(\theta)}{\rho(\theta)} = \frac{d\rho}{d\theta}\frac{d\theta}{ds} = \frac{d\rho}{ds} \tag{25}$$

is fundamental in the study of those properties of curves that are not changed in any similitude. From (24) we have

Corollary 1.3.   *For any oval with differentiable curvature and any given angle γ there are at least four solutions* (distinct if $\gamma \neq \pi$) *to*

$$\frac{d\rho}{ds}(\theta) = \frac{d\rho}{ds}(\theta + \gamma).$$

In order to simplify our next statements, we shall use "f is a 4 extrema function" for "$f(\theta)$ has at least two relative maxima and two relative minima in $0 \leqslant \theta \leqslant 2\pi$."

If we put the origin of the coordinate system at the mass centroid of the oval, (18) shows that r^3 (and hence r) is a 4 extrema function. At an extremum, $r' = 0$, hence $h' = 0$ by (8) and $r = h$ by (7). The last equation says that the radius vector is perpendicular to the tangent if r is maximal or minimal:

Corollary 1.4.   *From its mass centroid, at least four normals can be drawn to an oval.*

For instance, the center of a circle is the only point from which more than two normals can be drawn to the circle.

Corollary 1.5.   *Let r_1, r_2 be the radii vectors of two ovals measured from the respective mass centroids. Then r_1/r_2 is a 4 extrema function.*

The same argument as that leading to Corollary 1.4, if applied to (20), shows:

Corollary 1.6.   *From its curvature centroid, at least four normals can be drawn to an oval.*

Equation (21) also yields interesting results. In polar coordinates of center P,

$$\mu x \, ds = \frac{r(\phi)\sqrt{r^2 + (dr/d\theta)^2}}{\rho(\phi) \, h^2(\theta(\phi))} \cos \phi \, d\phi = \frac{1}{\rho \sin^3 \alpha} \cos \phi \, d\phi,$$

$$\mu y \, ds = \frac{r(\phi)\sqrt{r^2 + (dr/d\theta)^2}}{\rho(\phi) \, h^2(\theta(\theta))} \sin \phi \, d\phi = \frac{1}{\rho \sin^3 \alpha} \sin \phi \, d\phi.$$

Corollary 1.7. *The function $\rho \sin^3 \alpha$ is a 4 extrema function.* The function $1/\rho h^3$ is very important in the study of those properties of curves that are not changed in transformations of the plane of equations

$$\xi = ax + by, \qquad \eta = cx + dy, \qquad ad - bc = 1.$$

It is called the "unimodular centro-affine curvature," and, in general, is not a 4 extrema function (e.g., not for the circle if the origin is not the center of the circle). But for P at the mass centroid we may put

$$f = \frac{1}{\rho \sin^3 \alpha} = \frac{r^3}{\rho h^3} \qquad g = r^3.$$

Corollary 1.8. *The unimodular centro-affine curvature for the mass centroid of an oval is a 4 extrema function.*

We may note that $\sin \alpha$ is a 4 extrema function for any origin, since by the argument preceding Corollary 1.4 at least twice $\sin \alpha = 1$.

The reader will be able to find many more 4 extrema functions that may be suggested by symbols like

$$\frac{r_1^3(\theta)}{h_2(\theta + \gamma)}, \qquad \frac{\rho_1(\theta)}{r_2^3(\theta + \gamma)}, \qquad h_1(\theta)\rho_2(\theta) \sin^3 \alpha_2(\theta),$$

and so on.

3. MEAN VALUE THEOREMS

Theorem 2.   If $f(\theta)$ is continuous, periodic of period 2π, and

$$\int_0^{2\pi} f(\theta) \cos \theta \, d\theta = \int_0^{2\pi} f(\theta) \sin \theta \, d\theta = 0,$$

then

$$f(\theta) = \bar{f}$$

at least four times in the interval $0 < \theta \leqslant 2\pi$.

PROOF: The function

$$F(\theta) = \int_0^{\theta} (f(\tau) - \bar{f}) \, dt$$

is periodic of period 2π since its derivative is periodic and

$$F(2\pi) = \int_0^{2\pi} f(\theta) \, d\theta - 2\pi \bar{f} = 0 = F(0).$$

Also

$$\int_0^{2\pi} F(\theta) \cos \theta \, d\theta = \int_0^{2\pi} \left\{ \int_0^{\theta} f(\tau) \, d\tau \right\} \cos \theta \, d\theta - \bar{f} \int_0^{2\pi} \theta \cos \theta \, d\theta,$$

$$\int_0^{2\pi} F(\theta) \sin \theta \, d\theta = \int_0^{2\pi} \left\{ \int_0^{\theta} f(\tau) \, d\tau \right\} \sin \theta \, d\theta - \bar{f} \int_0^{2\pi} \theta \sin \theta \, d\theta.$$

But

$$\int_0^{2\pi} \left\{ \int_0^{\theta} f(\tau) \, d\tau \right\} \cos \theta \, d\theta = - \int_0^{2\pi} f(\theta) \sin \theta \, d\theta = 0,$$

$$\int_0^{2\pi} \theta \cos \theta \, d\theta = - \int_0^{2\pi} \sin \theta \, d\theta = 0,$$

$$\int_0^{2\pi} \left\{ \int_0^{\theta} f(\tau) \, d\tau \right\} \sin \theta \, d\theta = -2\pi \bar{f} + \int_0^{2\pi} f(\theta) \cos \theta \, d\theta = -2\pi \bar{f},$$

$$\int_0^{2\pi} \theta \sin \theta \, d\theta = -2\pi \bar{f} + \bar{f} \int_0^{2\pi} \cos \theta \, d\theta = -2\pi \bar{f}.$$

Hence,

$$\int_0^{2\pi} F(\theta) \cos \theta \, d\theta = \int_0^{2\pi} F(\theta) \sin \theta \, d\theta = 0$$

and, by Theorem 1, $F(\theta)$ is a 4 extrema function. Since $F(\theta)$ is periodic, all extrema occur at interior points of its domain of definition. Hence at least four times

$$F'(\theta) = f(\theta) - \bar{f} = 0. \qquad \blacksquare$$

The circle of curvature is defined in elementary calculus as a circle tangent to the curve whose radius is the radius of curvature at that point. The mean value of the radius of curvature is

$$\bar{\rho} = \frac{1}{2\pi} \int_0^{2\pi} \rho \, d\theta = \frac{1}{2\pi} \int_0^{2\pi} ds(\theta) = \frac{L}{2\pi}.$$

Corollary 2.1. Any oval has at least four circles of curvature whose perimeters equal the perimeter of the curve.

Here we consider two circles of curvature as distinct if they belong to two different points of contact; they may coincide as point sets.

One defines the *polar moment of degree n* of a plane area with respect to the origin as

$$I_n = \int_0^{2\pi} \int_0^{r(\theta)} r^n \, r \, dr \, d\theta. \qquad (26)$$

Hence

$$\bar{r} = \frac{3}{2\pi} I_1,$$

and *the equation*

$$r(\theta) = \frac{3}{2\pi} I_1$$

has at least four distinct solutions θ if the origin is placed at the mass centroid.

This result can be given a slightly more interesting turn. The *diameter* D of an oval is the length of a maximal chord, hence

$$D \geqslant r(\theta) + r(\theta + \pi)$$

if the origin is in the interior. The function $R(\theta) = r^3(\theta) + r^3(\theta + \pi)$ satisfies the conditions of Theorem 2 if the origin is at the mass centroid, and its mean value is $\bar{R} = (3/\pi)I_1$. This uses the fundamental facts, that for any periodic function $f(\theta)$ and constant γ

$$\int_0^\theta f(\theta)\, d\theta = \int_0^\theta f(\theta + \gamma)\, d\theta,$$

or

$$\overline{f(\theta) + f(\theta + \gamma)} = 2\bar{f}, \tag{27}$$

$$\overline{f(\theta) - f(\theta + \gamma)} = 0. \tag{28}$$

Also, if $f(\theta)$ satisfies the hypotheses of Theorem 2, so does $g(\theta) = f(\theta + \gamma)$. On the other hand, $r(\theta) + r(\theta + \pi) \geqslant R(\theta)^{1/3}$ for $r(\theta) \geqslant 0$.

Corollary 2.2.   *The diameter of an oval is* $> (3I_1/\pi)^{1/3}$, *the moment being computed for the mass centroid.*

The *width* $w(\theta)$ *in direction* $\theta + (\pi/2)$ is the distance of the two tangent lines of angles $\theta, \theta + \pi$. The *width* W *of the oval* is the minimum of $w(\theta)$. A curve is of *constant width* if $W = w(\theta)$ for all θ. If the origin is in the interior of the oval,

$$W \leqslant w(\theta) = h(\theta) + h(\theta + \pi), \qquad h(\theta) > 0.$$

By (14)

$$W \leqslant \bar{w} = L/\pi. \tag{29}$$

If the origin is placed at the curvature centroid, $h(\theta)$ and $w(\theta)$ satisfy the hypotheses of Theorem 2. In the next statement, "direction" means "direction of unoriented line."

Corollary 2.3.   *For any oval there exist at least two distinct directions for which the width equals the width of a circle whose perimeter equals the perimeter of the curve.*

Corollary 2.4.   *The perimeter of a curve of constant width W is $L = \pi W$.*

From (28), results like the following are obtained.

Corollary 2.5.   *Let $r(\theta)$ be measured from the mass centroid, $h(\theta)$ from the curvature centroid of an oval, and let γ be an arbitrary constant. Each of the equations*

$$\rho(\theta) = \rho(\theta + \gamma),$$

$$r(\theta) = r(\theta + \gamma),$$

$$h(\theta) = h(\theta + \gamma)$$

has at least four distinct solutions in $0 \leqslant \theta < 2\pi$.

Considering $\overline{\rho_1(\theta) - \rho_2(\theta)}$, we have

Corollary 2.6.   *Two ovals of same perimeter L have equal curvature radii for at least four distinct directions.*

There are similar results for $r(\theta)$ and $h(\theta)$. The last result is particularly interesting if the curvature centroids of the ovals coincide because then equality of the support function means identity of the tangents.

Corollary 2.7.   *Any two ovals of equal perimeter and identical curvature centroids have at least four common tangents.*

Let us call the two ovals C_1 and C_2, respectively. Four of the common tangents form a quadrilateral circumscribed to C_1; C_2 is closed and must have points in at least two of the triangular domains that make up the quadrilateral outside the oval C_1, unless all points of contact of C_1 and the tangents are also points of C_2 (Figure 5-2).

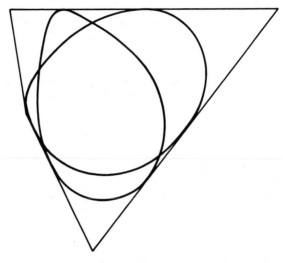

FIG. 5-2

Corollary 2.8.   *Any two ovals of equal perimeter and identical curvature centroids have at least four common points.*

Hence if C_2 results from C_1 by a rotation about the curvature centroid, C_2 and C_1 intersect at least four times.

Since in real numbers $r_1{}^3 = r_2{}^3$ implies $r_1 = r_2$, we also have

Corollary 2.9.   *Any two ovals of equal moments I_1 (referred to the mass centroid) and identical mass centroids have at least four common points.*

$h'(\theta)$ is the distance from the origin of the normal to the curve in $[x(\theta), y(\theta)]$ [see (7)]. Given two ovals C_1 and C_2,

$$E(\theta) = h_1'(\theta) - h_2'(\theta) \qquad \text{and} \qquad F(\theta) = h_1'(\theta) + h_2'(\theta + \pi)$$

are the distances of the pairs of parallel normals to C_1 and C_2 whose orientations are, respectively, equal or opposite. (Here we consider the normals as images of the oriented tangents by a rotation of $+\pi/2$.) By (13), $\bar{E} = \bar{F} = 0$. If the origin is at the common curvature centroid of C_1 and C_2, E and F satisfy the hypotheses of Theorem 2 since

$$\int_0^{2\pi} h'(\theta) \cos \theta \, d\theta = \int_0^{2\pi} h(\theta) \sin \theta \, d\theta,$$

$$\int_0^{2\pi} h'(\theta) \sin \theta \, d\theta = - \int_0^{2\pi} h(\theta) \cos \theta \, d\theta.$$

Corollary 2.10.   *Two ovals with identical curvature centroids have at least four common normals with equal orientations and four common normals with opposite orientations* (under the counting convention of Corollary 2.1).

4. PARALLEL TANGENTS

Theorem 3.   *Under the hypotheses of Theorem 2, there are at least three distinct solutions to*

$$f(\theta) = f(\theta + \pi), \qquad 0 \leqslant \theta < \pi.$$

For the proof we consider the function

$$D(\theta) = f(\theta) - f(\theta + \pi).$$

Since $D(\pi) = -D(0)$, it follows by Bolzano's theorem that D has at least one root θ_0 in the interval $0 < \theta \leqslant \pi$. By the remark after (28), we may choose our system of coordinates so that $\theta_0 = \pi/2$. Also

$$\int_0^{2\pi} f(\theta) \cos \theta \, d\theta = \int_0^{\pi} D(\theta) \cos \theta \, d\theta$$

$$= \int_0^{\pi/2} \left[D(\theta) \cos \theta - D\left(\theta + \frac{\pi}{2}\right) \sin \theta \right] d\theta = 0,$$

$$\tag{30}$$

$$\int_0^{2\pi} f(\theta) \sin \theta \, d\theta = \int_0^{\pi} D(\theta) \sin \theta \, d\theta$$

$$= \int_0^{\pi/2} \left[D(\theta) \sin \theta + D\left(\theta + \frac{\pi}{2}\right) \cos \theta \right] d\theta = 0.$$

$$\tag{31}$$

Assume first that $D(0) \neq 0$. Since $D(\pi) = -D(0)$, the graph of $D = D(\theta)$ must cross the θ-axis an odd number of times in $0 < \theta < \pi$. If $\pi/2$ were the only zero of D in the interval, then it would follow that

$$0 \neq \text{sign } D(\theta) = -\text{sign } D\left(\theta + \frac{\pi}{2}\right), \qquad 0 < \theta < \frac{\pi}{2}, \qquad (32)$$

hence

$$\int_0^{\pi/2} \left[D(\theta) \cos \theta - D\left(\theta + \frac{\pi}{2}\right) \sin \theta \right] d\theta > 0,$$

in contradiction to (30). Therefore, $D(\theta)$ has at least three zeroes.

If $D(0) = D(\pi) = 0$, then for the same reason as before it is impossible that (32) hold. Therefore, there will be at least three roots in the interval unless

$$0 \neq \text{sign } D(\theta) = \text{sign } D(\theta + \pi/2), \qquad 0 < \theta < \pi/2.$$

But this, then, contradicts (31).

Corollary 3.1.   *On any oval there exist at least three distinct pairs of points for which the tangents are parallel* (with opposite orientations) *and the radii of curvature are equal.*

If $r(\theta) = r(\theta + \pi)$, the origin bisects the secant in direction θ.

Corollary 3.2.   *At least three chords of an oval are bisected at its mass centroid.*

If $h(\theta) = h(\theta + \pi)$, the tangents are equidistant from the origin. The same holds for normals if $h(\theta) = h'(\theta + \pi)$.

Corollary 3.3.   *At least three pairs of parallel tangents* (normals) *of an oval are equidistant from the curvature centroid.*

BIBLIOGRAPHY AND HISTORY

The problems in this paper are all of recent origin. Therefore, it seems possible to give the names of the first discoverers and a fairly complete bibliography.

1860 E. Barbier, "Note sur le problème de l'aiguille et le jeu du joint ouvert." *J. Math. pures appl.* (2) 5, 1860, 273–286. (Cor. 2.4. The literature dealing with the properties of curves of constant width is very vast.)

1903 A. Hurwitz, "Über die Fourierschen Konstanten integrierbarer Funktionen." *Math. Ann.* 57, 1903, 425–446 (which contains a very general theorem from which Thm. 1 in the case $g = 1$, and Thms. 2 and 3 can be derived).

1909 S. Mukhopadhyaya, "New methods in the geometry of a plane arc." *Bull. Calcutta Math. Soc.* 1, 1909, 31–37 (Cor. 1.2).

E. Meissner, "Über die Anwendung von Fourier-Reihen auf einige Aufgaben der Geometrie und Kinematik." *Naturf. Ges. Zürich* 54, 1909, 309–329 (Cor. 2.6, 2.7, 2.8, 2.10).

1917 W. Blaschke, Aufgabe 540, *Arch. Math. Phys.* (3) 26, 1917, 65 (Cor. 3.1).

1924 W. Blaschke, *Differentialgeometrie I*. Springer Verlag, Berlin, 1924 (contains a proof of Cor. 1.2 due to G. Herglotz which is the model of the proof of Thm. 1).

W. Süss, "Lösung der Aufgabe 540" im *Arch. Math. Phys.* 26, J. Ber. D.M.V. 33, 1924, 32–33 (Thm. 3, Cor. 3.1).

1926 T. Hayashi, "Some geometrical applications of Fourier series." *Rend. Circ. Mat. Palermo*, 1, 1926, 96–102 (Cor. 1.6, Thm. 2, Cor. 2.1, 2.3).

1927 W. Süss, "Zur relativen Differentialgeometrie I." *Japan J. Math.* 4, 1927, 57–76 (Cor. 1.1).

1935 R. C. Bose, "A note on the convex oval." *Bull. Calcutta Math. Soc.* 27, 1935, 54–60 (Cor. 1.4, 3.2, 3.3. Bose also proves significant complements to these results).

1966 O. Haupt, H. Kunneth, *Geometrische Ordnungen*. Springer Verlag, Berlin, 1966 (topological theory of four theorems, without differentiability).

The remaining results (Thm. 1, Cor. 1.3, 1.5, 1.7, 1.8, 2.2, 2.5, 2.9) seem to be new. See also *Am. Math. Monthly* 71, 1964, Problem 5197, p. 441, and *Elemente der Math.* 21, 1966, Aufgabe 493, p. 17–18.

The research for this paper was partially supported by the U.S. Air Force Office of Scientific Research.

6

Additive Functions

ALBERT WILANSKY

LEHIGH UNIVERSITY

A native of St. John's, Newfoundland, Albert Wilansky
earned his Ph.D. at Brown University in 1947. After
teaching at Dalhousie and Brown he came to Lehigh
University where he is now Professor of Mathematics.
He was a consultant at the Frankford Arsenal and is
presently Associate Editor of the *American Mathematical
Monthly*. His research publications are in functional and
classical analysis, topology, and summability. He has also
contributed many teaching notes, problems, and solutions
to collegiate journals, and assisted in the compilation of
the *Otto Dunkel Memorial Problem Book*. He is the
author of *Functional Analysis*.

In his lecture on additive functions, Professor Wilansky introduces the student to some important ideas of the
modern theory of functions of a real variable and functional analysis.

ADDITIVE FUNCTIONS

Albert Wilansky

1. ADDITIVE FUNCTIONS

All functions in this essay are real valued functions of a real variable; thus each $f : R \to R$, where R is the set of real numbers. An *additive* function f is one which satisfies

$$f(x + y) = f(x) + f(y), \qquad \text{for all } x, y. \qquad (1)$$

The only examples of additive functions which come readily to mind are multiples of the independent variable; thus, if k is a number, and we define f by

$$f(x) = kx, \qquad \text{for all } x, \qquad (2)$$

then f is additive. The question arises, are there any other additive functions?

DEFINITION: A function satisfying (2) for some k will be called linear.

We begin by showing that the only *continuous* additive functions are those which are linear, a result first proved by A. Cauchy

I wish to thank Professors G. F. Feeman and G. Rayna for assistance in searching the literature and for helpful discussions.

in 1821. A preliminary remark is that (2) does reveal one characteristic of all additive functions:

> *Lemma* 1.　*If f is additive, $f(0) = 0$.*
> For $f(0) = f(0 + 0) = f(0) + f(0) = 2f(0)$.

> *Theorem* 1.　*Let f be a continuous additive function. Then f is linear.*

We shall give two proofs of Theorem 1. The first is brief and involves calculus. The second is more instructive and elementary, though longer. It will appear following Corollary 1 to Theorem 2 in Section 2. As we will see, Theorem 1 will also follow from many similar results in which continuity is replaced by weaker assumptions; examples are Theorems 5, 6, 7, and 14.

Fix x, and write

$$\int_0^1 f(x + y)\, dy = \int_0^1 [f(x) + f(y)]\, dy$$

$$= f(x) + \int_0^1 f(y)\, dy.$$

Make the substitution $u = x + y$ in the first integral and it becomes

$$\int_x^{1+x} f(u)\, du.$$

Thus the above computation becomes

$$f(x) = \int_x^{1+x} f(u)\, du - \int_0^1 f(y)\, dy$$

Differentiation yields

$$f'(x) = f(1 + x) - f(x).$$

Since f is additive, this yields $f'(x) = f(1)$. It follows that $f(x) = f(1)x + C$ and Lemma 1 shows that $C = 0$. This completes the first proof of Theorem 1, revealing the obvious and expected fact that $k = f(1)$.

2. HOMOGENEITY

We can obtain the conclusion of Theorem 1 from a different sort of assumption. Let us call a function f *homogeneous* if

$$f(ax) = af(x), \qquad \text{for all } a, x. \tag{3}$$

If f is homogeneous, we may set $x = 1$ in (3) and conclude that f is linear. We shall occasionally use the obvious fact that condition (2) implies condition (3). We now see that every additive function satisfies a condition similar to (3):

Theorem 2. Let f be an additive function. Then f is rationally homogeneous, i.e., (3) holds for all x and all rational a.

For any x,

$$f(2x) = f(x + x) = f(x) + f(x) = 2f(x);$$

hence

$$f(3x) = f(2x + x) = f(2x) + f(x) = 2f(x) + f(x) = 3f(x);$$

and so in general

$$f(nx) = nf(x) \text{ if } n \text{ is a positive integer.} \tag{4}$$

Next we observe that $f(x) + f(-x) = f[x + (-x)] = f(0) = 0$ by Lemma 1, and so

$$f(-x) = -f(x). \tag{5}$$

If n is a negative integer, $f(nx) = -f(-nx)$ [by (5)] $= -f[(-n)x] = -(-n)f(x)$ [by (4)] $= nf(x)$, so we have

$$f(nx) = nf(x), \qquad \text{for all } x, \text{ and all integer } n. \tag{6}$$

Finally, let a be a rational number, say $a = m/n$ where m, n are integers. Then $nf(ax) = f(nax)$ [by (6)] $= f(mx) = mf(x)$ [by (6)], and so

$$f(ax) = \frac{m}{n} f(x) = af(x),$$

This result enables us to approximate the result of Theorem 1:

Corollary 1.   Let f be additive. Then there exists a number k such that $f(x) = kx$ for all rational x.

By Theorem 2, (3) holds for rational a. Setting $x = 1$ yields $f(a) = ka$ for all rational a, where $k = f(1)$. This is clearly equivalent to the conclusion of Corollary 1.

The second proof of Theorem 1 is now at hand. Let f be additive and continuous and let $k = f(1)$. For any real number x we can find a sequence $\{a_n\}$ of rational numbers with $a_n \to x$. From Corollary 1, $f(a_n) = ka_n$ for all n. Since f is continuous, $f(a_n) \to f(x)$ while $ka_n \to kx$. Thus $f(x) = kx$. A briefer version of this proof runs: the difference $f(x) - kx$ is continuous, vanishes for rational x, hence everywhere.)

$\triangle$ REMARK:[†]   Corollary 1 shows that an additive function with closed graph is continuous. In general an additive map with closed graph between linear topological spaces is real linear.

3. PROPERTIES OF NON-LINEAR ADDITIVE FUNCTIONS

So far all the evidence points to the truth of Theorem 1 with the word "continuous" omitted. We shall see in Section 7 that this conjecture is false, but in the meantime we obtain further supporting evidence by noting the highly pathological behavior of a non-linear additive function, supposing that one should exist.

Theorem 3.   An additive function which is discontinuous at one point must be discontinuous everywhere. Equivalently, an additive function which is continuous at one point must be continuous everywhere.

Suppose that f is additive and continuous at t. Let x be

† Note: Parts marked $\triangle$ are deeper and may be omitted.

arbitrary. Then $|f(x + h) - f(x)| = |f(h)| = |f(t + h) - f(t)|$; from this it is clear that f is continuous at x.

Corollary 2.   *If an additive function is continuous at one point, it is linear.*

But an additive non-linear function must have a property far more pathological than that expressed by Theorem 3:

Theorem 4.   *Let f be a non-linear additive function. Then the graph of f is dense in the plane, i.e., every circle contains a point, (x, y) such that $y = f(x)$.*

REMARK 1:   A greatly abbreviated proof of Theorem 4 is given in the Appendix at the end of this article.

△ REMARK 2:   Let $h(x, y) = y - f(x)$. Then h is a rational linear function and Theorems 1 and 4 say that $h^{\perp}$ is either closed or dense. This is very reminiscent of standard theorems on linear functionals (see, for example, [27] Section 10.5, Theorem 3, and Corollary 3).

REMARK 3:   Notice that the graph of an additive continuous function is, by Theorem 1, a straight line; this certainly does not have the density property given here. The pathological nature of the graph is emphasized by the fact that it meets each vertical line exactly once; namely, it meets the line $x = a$ in the point $[a, f(a)]$. This seems at first glance inconsistent with Theorem 4.

To simplify the proof of Theorem 4 we give two preliminary lemmas.

Lemma 2.   *Let g be a function whose graph is dense in the plane, let p be a non-zero number, and let $f = p \cdot g$. Then the graph of f is dense in the plane.*

Let C be a circle, say with center (x, y) and radius $r > 0$. Let C' be the circle with center $(x, y/p)$ and radius $r' = r/(1 + p^2)^{1/2}$. There exists a point (a, b) with $b = g(a)$ in the circle C' since the graph of g is dense. But then the point (a, pb) lies in the circle C since

$$(a - x)^2 + (pb - y)^2 = (a - x)^2 + p^2(b - (y/p))^2 \leqslant r'^2 + p^2r'^2$$

since

$$(a - x)^2 \leqslant (a - x)^2 + (b - (y/b))^2 \leqslant r'^2$$

and $(b - (y/b))^2 \leqslant r'^2$ for the same reason; thus

$$(a - x)^2 + (pb - y)^2 \leqslant (1 + p^2)r'^2 = r^2.$$

Moreover, $pb = f(a)$ and so (a, pb) belongs to the graph of f.

Lemma 3. *Let g be a function whose graph is dense in the plane, let k be a number, and let $f(x) = g(x) + kx$ for all x. Then the graph of f is dense in the plane.*

Let C be a circle with center (x, y) and radius $r > 0$. Let C' be the circle with center $(x, y - ka)$ and radius r. There exists a point (a, b) with $b = g(a)$ in the circle C'. But then the point $(a, b + ka)$ lies in the circle C since

$$(a - x)^2 + (b + ka - y)^2 \leqslant r^2.$$

Moreover $b + ka = f(a)$ and so $(a, b + ka)$ belongs to the graph of f.

To complete the proof of Theorem 4, let f be an additive discontinuous function, and let $k = f(1)$. There must be a number t such that $f(t) \neq kt$, for if this were not so, Equation (2) would hold and f would be linear.

Let

$$g(x) = \frac{f(x) - kx}{f(t) - kt}.$$

Then g is the difference of two additive functions divided by a constant; thus g is itself additive. Moreover, g has the convenient property that $g(1) = 0$ and hence that $g(x) = 0$ for all rational x, by Theorem 2.

We now show that the graph of g is dense in the plane. Let C be a circle with center (x, y) and radius $r > 0$. Choose a rational number v with $|v - y| < r/2$. Choose a rational number u with

$$|u - (x - vt)| < r/2.$$

Then $(u + vt, v)$ lies in C since

$$(u + vt - x)^2 + (v - y)^2 < r^2/4 + (r^2/4) < r^2.$$

Moreover, $(u + vt, v)$ belongs to the graph of g since

$$g(u + vt) = g(u) + g(vt) = ug(1) + vg(t) \text{ [by Theorem 2]} = v.$$

Theorem 4 now follows from Lemmas 2 and 3 and the fact that $f(x) = pg(x) + kx$ with $k = f(1)$ and $p = f(t) - kt$.

REMARK 4: As mentioned in Remark 3, the graph of g meets each vertical line once. However, if v is rational, the graph of g meets the horizontal line $y = v$ in a set which is dense in that line, since $g(u + vt) = v$ for all rational u.

4. CRITERIA FOR LINEARITY

Since non-linear additive functions must, if they exist, be so badly behaved, we can list some very slight conditions which imply that an additive function is linear.

Theorem 5.   Let f be an additive function. If f satisfies any one of the following conditions, then f is linear.

(a) *There exists an interval on which f is bounded above;*

(b) *there exists an interval on which f is bounded below;*

(c) *there exists an interval on which f is monotone, i.e., f is either increasing throughout the interval or decreasing throughout the interval;*

(d) *there exists an interval I such that $\{f(x) : x \text{ in } I\}$ is not a dense subset of the real line.*

Each of the listed conditions implies the existence of a circle containing no point of the graph of f. If (a) holds, say $f(x) \leqslant m$ for $a \leqslant x \leqslant b$, the graph of f does not meet

$$\{(x, y) : a \leqslant x \leqslant b, y > m\},$$

a set which contains a circle of radius $\frac{1}{2}(b - a)$. If (c) holds, f is bounded on some smaller interval. If (d) holds, let $I = [a, b]$ and suppose that $[c, d]$ is an interval containing no $f(x)$, $a \leqslant x \leqslant b$. Then the graph of f contains no points of the rectangle $a \leqslant x \leqslant b$, $c \leqslant y \leqslant d$.

Theorem 6.   *Let f be an additive and multiplicative function* $[f(xy) = f(x)f(y).]$ *Then f is linear.*

For any positive number x,

$$f(x) = f(\sqrt{x} \cdot \sqrt{x}) = f(\sqrt{x}) \cdot f(\sqrt{x}) = [f(\sqrt{x})]^2 \geqslant 0.$$

The result now follows from Theorem 5, part (b).

REMARK 1:   For the proof of Theorem 6 we used the multiplicative property only in the form $f(a^2) = [f(a)]^2$. However, consideration of the identity

$$ab = \tfrac{1}{4}[(a + b)^2 - (a - b)^2]$$

shows that an additive function satisfying this condition is multiplicative, even under far more general assumptions about its domain.

REMARK 2:   If f obeys the hypotheses of Theorem 6,

$$f(1) = f(1^2) = [f(1)]^2.$$

Thus $f(1) = 0$ or 1. It follows from Theorem 1 that $f = 0$ or $f(x) = x$ for all x.

REMARK 3:   An interesting formulation of Theorem 6 is that if $f(x)$ and $\log f(e^x)$ are both additive, then f is linear.

REMARK 4: (Complex functions.) It is surprising that Theorem 6 fails for complex functions. Indeed there is a discontinuous automorphism of the complex plane (it is one-to-one, onto, additive, and multiplicative); see [15]. Concerning complex valued functions of a real variable, it has been pointed out by Dharmadhikari [4] that although Theorem 2 holds, the following equivalent formulation fails if f is allowed to have complex values: *For a non-zero real function f on R satisfying $f(x + y) = f(x)f(y)$ for all x, y, there exists k such that $f(r) = e^{kr}$ for all rational r.* We first see that $f(x) > 0$ for all x, for

$$f(x) = f(\tfrac{1}{2}x + \tfrac{1}{2}x) = [f(\tfrac{1}{2}x)]^2 \geqslant 0,$$

and if $f(a) = 0$ for some a, then, for all x,

$$f(x) = f(a + x - a) = f(a)f(x - a) = 0.$$

Now let $g(x) = \log f(x)$. Then g is additive, and the result follows from Theorem 2. [Set $x = 1$ and replace f by g in (3); $k = \log f(1)$.]

A set which is the intersection of a sequence of open sets is called a G_δ set. Since every closed set in R^2 is a G_δ, the following result generalizes the Remark of Section 2.

$\triangle$ *Theorem 7. Let f be an additive function such that the graph of f is a G_δ. Then f is linear.*

Suppose that the graph $G = \cap \, G_n$, each G_n being open. The closure $\bar{G}$ of G in R^2 is a linear subspace of R^2 considered as a linear space over the field of rationals, since by Theorem 2, G is such a subspace. (See [27], Section 10.2, Theorem 1(c).) Each G_n is a dense open subset of $\bar{G}$ and so each $\bar{G}\backslash G_n$ (the complement of G_n in $\bar{G}$) is nowhere dense in $\bar{G}$. (This is understood from now on.) Thus $\bar{G}\backslash G$ is σ-nowhere dense (the union of a sequence of nowhere dense sets; "of first category" as it is usually called). But for any x in $\bar{G}\backslash G$ we have $x + G \subset \bar{G}\backslash G$ and so $x + G$, and hence G, is of first category. Thus, $\bar{G}$ is of first category; but it is a complete metric space, which cannot be of first category ([27], 5.3, Theorem 1).

Thus, no such x can exist; $G = \bar{G}$; that is, G is closed and the result follows from the Remark of Section 2.

$\triangle$ *Corollary 3. Let f be an additive function such that the graph of f can be given a complete metric yielding the Euclidean topology. Then f is linear.*

For the graph is, then, a G_δ. See [16], p.207, Problem K.

It should be noted that the existence of such a complete metric is not as much of a restriction as one might expect, for example, the space of irrational numbers, being a G_δ (since the set of rationals is obviously an $F\sigma$) allows such a metric.

In Section 8 we shall return to an examination of conditions sufficient for linearity; it is time to interrupt this program for a display of the existence of non-linear additive functions.

5. HAMEL BASES

Suppose we let S stand for the set of all numbers of the form $u + v \cdot \sqrt{2} + w \cdot \sqrt{3}$, where u, v, w are rational. Then S contains the numbers 1, $\sqrt{2}$, $\sqrt{3}$, $5\sqrt{2} - \frac{1}{2}\sqrt{3}$ and infinitely many others. The remark of greatest significance is that each member of S is a *rational linear combination* of 1, $\sqrt{2}$, $\sqrt{3}$, i.e., is of the form $u \cdot 1 + v \cdot \sqrt{2} + w \cdot \sqrt{3}$ with u, v, w rational; but more is true: each member of S is a *unique* rational linear combination of 1, $\sqrt{2}$, $\sqrt{3}$. This means that if

$$u + v\sqrt{2} + w\sqrt{3} = u' + v'\sqrt{2} + w'\sqrt{3}$$

with u, v, w, u', v', w' all rational, then $u = u'$, $v = v'$, $w = w'$. To prove this we note that this assumption implies that

$$(u - u') + (v - v')\sqrt{2} + (w - w')\sqrt{3} = 0,$$

and so our problem is reduced to showing that if $a + b\sqrt{2} + c\sqrt{3} = 0$; a, b, c rational, then $a = b = c = 0$. Rewriting the assumed equation as $b\sqrt{2} + c\sqrt{3} = -a$, squaring, and transposing, we obtain $2bc\sqrt{6} = a^2 - 2b^2 - 3c^2$. This implies that either b or c is zero for if neither b nor c is zero, we may divide both sides by $2bc$ and have an equation expressing $\sqrt{6}$ as a rational number. (If the reader wishes to prove that $\sqrt{6}$ is not rational, he may write $\sqrt{6} = m/n$, m, n integers. This yields $m^2 = 6n^2$. Factoring m^2 into prime factors yields an even number, perhaps zero, of 2's. The same is true for n^2 so that $6n^2$ contains an odd number of 2's. Thus $m^2 = 6n^2$ is impossible.)

We have now proved that either b or c is 0. If $b = 0$, we have $a + c\sqrt{3} = 0$; this implies that $c = 0$ for if $c \neq 0$, we would have $\sqrt{3} = -a/c$, a rational number. Similarly if $c = 0$, we obtain that $b = 0$. Thus both b, c are zero. It follows immediately that $a = 0$.

DEFINITION: *Let S be a set of real numbers and let B be a subset of S. Then B is called a Hamel basis for S if every member of S is a unique (finite) rational linear combination of B.*

Thus if B is a Hamel basis for S and x is a member of S, there are numbers b_1, b_2, ..., b_n in B and rational numbers r_1, r_2, ..., r_n such that $s = r_1 b_1 + r_2 b_2 + \cdots + r_n b_n$. Moreover, the numbers b_1, b_2, ..., b_n, r_1, r_2, ..., r_n are uniquely determined by x, except for the order in which they are selected.

Our first example showed that if S is the set of all rational linear combinations of 1, $\sqrt{2}$, $\sqrt{3}$ and B is the set 1, $\sqrt{2}$, $\sqrt{3}$, then B is a Hamel basis for S.

Let us consider briefly a set with an infinite Hamel basis. Let e be the familiar base of natural logarithms, and let $B = \{1, e, e^2, e^3, \ldots\}$ and let S be the set of all (finite) rational linear combinations of B. Then B is a Hamel basis for S; this is difficult to prove; it requires us to show that if a_0, a_1, ..., a_n are rational and if $a_0 + a_1 e + \cdots + a_n e^n = 0$, then $a_0 = a_1 = \cdots = a_n = 0$, i.e., that e does not satisfy any non-trivial algebraic equation, i.e., that e is a so-called transcendental number. A proof is given in [11], pp. 176-178.

Suppose that we wished to construct a Hamel basis for the set of all real numbers. We begin by choosing an arbitrary non-zero number, say 1. Choose a number, say $\sqrt{2}$, which is not a rational multiple of 1. Choose a number, say $\sqrt{3}$, which is not a rational linear combination of $\{1, \sqrt{2}\}$. Continuing this process we have at each stage a set, none of whose members is a finite linear combination of the others. Let us call such a set *independent*. Continuing the process will never produce a Hamel basis since, as is indicated by the second example above, such a basis would have to be infinite. Before continuing this discussion, let us set our minds at rest by stating a result.

Theorem 8.   *There is a set which is a Hamel basis for the set R of all real numbers.*

The proof is suggested by the simple inductive process given just before the statement of the theorem. If we have an independent set B, either B is a Hamel basis or it is not. If it is not, we can select a real number which is not a rational linear combination of B; thus B, together with the new number, is a larger independent set. Hence a set B will be a Hamel basis if it is independent and maximal, i.e., is included in no larger independent set. We conclude the proof of Theorem 8 by asserting the existence of such a maximal set; supporting this assertion would take us beyond the scope of this article. See [27], Section 2.3, Theorem 1.

In Section 10 we shall give some indications of what properties a Hamel basis may have.

6. CONSTRUCTION OF ADDITIVE FUNCTIONS

There is an intimate connection between additive functions and Hamel bases. In fact, to exhibit an additive function it is sufficient to give its values on a Hamel basis, and, indeed, these values may be given arbitrarily. This is the content of the next two theorems.

Theorem 9.   *Let B be a Hamel basis for R. If two additive functions have the same value at each member of B, they are equal.*

If f_1 and f_2 are additive and have the same value at each member of B, then $f_1 - f_2$ is additive and is zero at each member of B. Thus the result will be proved if it is shown that an additive function must be zero if it vanishes on B. Let f be such a function. Let x be a real number; then there are numbers $b_1, b_2, \ldots, b_n$ in B and rational numbers $r_1, r_2, \ldots, r_n$ such that $x = r_1 b_1 + r_2 b_2 + \cdots + r_n b_n$.

It follows from Theorem 2 that

$$f(x) = r_1 f(b_1) + r_2 f(b_2) + \cdots + r_n f(b_n) = 0.$$

Thus $f = 0$.

Theorem 10.   *Let B be a Hamel basis for R. Let g be an arbitrary function defined on B. Then there exists an additive function f such that $f(b) = g(b)$ for each b in B.*

For each real number x there can be found $b_1, b_2, \ldots, b_n$ in B and rational numbers $r_1, r_2, \ldots, r_n$ with

$$x = r_1 b_1 + r_2 b_2 + \cdots + r_n b_n.$$

We define $f(x)$ to be

$$r_1 g(b_1) + r_2 g(b_2) + \cdots + r_n g(b_n).$$

This defines $f(x)$ for all x; note carefully that there is no ambiguity in this definition since, for each x, the choice of $b_1, b_2, \ldots, b_n, r_1, r_2, \ldots, r_n$ is unique, except for the order in which b_i and r_i are selected. For each b in B, $f(b) = g(b)$ by definition of f; it remains to show that f is additive. Let x, y be real numbers. Then

$$x = r_1 a_1 + r_2 a_2 + \cdots + r_n a_n, \quad y = s_1 b_1 + s_2 b_2 + \cdots + s_k b_k,$$

where $r_1, r_2, \ldots, r_n, s_1, s_2, \ldots, s_k$ are rational numbers and $a_1, a_2, \ldots, a_n, b_1, b_2, \ldots, b_k$ are members of B. The two sets $\{a_1, a_2, \ldots, a_n\}$ and $\{b_1, b_2, \ldots, b_k\}$ may have some members in common; let the union of these two sets be $\{c_1, c_2, \ldots, c_m\}$. Then $m \leqslant n + k$, and

$$x = u_1 c_1 + u_2 c_2 + \cdots + u_m c_m,$$

$$y = v_1 c_1 + v_2 c_2 + \cdots + v_m c_m,$$

where $u_1, u_2, \ldots, u_m, v_1, v_2, \ldots, v_m$ are rational numbers, several of which may be zero, for example, $u_1 = 0$ if c_1 is not one of the set $\{a_1, a_2, \ldots, a_n\}$, while if $c_1 = a_i$, say, then $u_1 = r_i$.

Now

$$x + y = (u_1 + v_1)c_1 + (u_2 + v_2)c_2 + \cdots + (u_m + v_m)c_m$$

and

$$f(x + y) = (u_1 + v_1)g(c_1) + (u_2 + v_2)g(c_2) + \cdots + (u_m + v_m)g(c_m)$$

$$= [u_1 g(c_1) + u_2 g(c_2) + \cdots + u_m g(c_m)]$$

$$+ [v_1 g(c_1) + v_2 g(c_2) + \cdots + v_m g(c_m)]$$

$$= f(x) + f(y).$$

Thus f is additive.

The construction given in the proof of Theorem 10 shows how to extend a function defined on a set B to an additive function. This was possible because of the special nature of B, but is not always possible. Consider, for example, a set S consisting of two numbers 1 and 2. Let $g(1) = 1$, $g(2) = 3$, thus defining a function g on S which cannot be extended to an additive function, since an additive function f must satisfy $f(2) = 2f(1)$ by Theorem 2. The next result gives conditions on g which allow it to be extended to an additive function. We shall make no further use of this result and shall give only a sketch of its proof.

Theorem 11.   *Let S be a set of real numbers and g a function defined on S such that whenever members $a_1, a_2, \ldots, a_n$ of S and rational numbers $r_1, r_2, \ldots, r_n$ are chosen such that*

$$r_1 a_1 + r_2 a_2 + \cdots r_n a_n = 0,$$

it follows that

$$r_1 g(a_1) + r_2 g(a_2) + \cdots + r_n g(a_n) = 0.$$

Then g can be extended to an additive function defined on R. In particular, this is true for arbitrary g if S is independent since in that case all the rationals selected must be zero.

Let C be the set of all rational linear combinations of S. For x in C,

$$x = r_1 a_1 + r_2 a_2 + \cdots + r_n a_n,$$

define

$$f(x) = r_1 g(a_1) + r_2 g(a_2) + \cdots + r_n g(a_n).$$

It may be that $a_1, a_2, \ldots, a_n$ are not uniquely determined by x, but if also

$$x = s_1 b_1 + s_2 b_2 + \cdots + s_k b_k,$$

we may, by the device used in the proof of Theorem 10, write

$$x = u_1 c_1 + u_2 c_2 + \cdots + u_m c_m$$
$$= v_1 c_1 + v_2 c_2 + \cdots + v_m c_m.$$

Then

$$0 = x - x = (u_1 - v_1) c_1 + \cdots + (u_m - v_m) c_m;$$

by hypothesis

$$(u_1 - v_1) g(c_1) + \cdots + (u_m - v_m) g(c_m) = 0,$$

i.e.,

$$u_1 g(c_1) + u_2 g(c_2) + \cdots + u_m g(c_m) = v_1 g(c_1) + v_2 g(c_2) + \cdots v_m g(c_m).$$

Thus the value given to $f(x)$ is uniquely determined. As in the proof of Theorem 10, f is shown to be additive. So far, f is defined only on C. A Hamel base is chosen for C and extended to a Hamel base B for the set of all real numbers.

For any real number x,

$$x = w_1 z_1 + w_2 z_2 + \cdots + w_p z_p,$$

with $z_1, z_2, \ldots, z_p$ in B and rational $w_1, w_2, \ldots, w_p$. Let y be the sum of those $w_i z_i$ for which z_i is in C. If all the z_i lie outside of C, let $y = 0$. Define $f_0(x) = f(y)$. This defines a function f_0 which is an extension of f, hence of g, and is easily seen to be additive.

7. CONSTRUCTION OF NON-LINEAR ADDITIVE FUNCTIONS

With the aid of a Hamel basis, a non-linear additive function is easy to construct. Let B be a Hamel basis for R, and let b be one of its members. Define a function g on B by $g(b) = 1$, $g(x) = 0$ for all other x in B; extend g to an additive function f by Theorem 10. Then for $x \varepsilon B$, $x \neq b$, we have

$$0 = \frac{f(x)}{x} \neq \frac{f(b)}{b}$$

so that f is non-linear.

It is clear that our particular choice of g could be varied; the resulting additive function will be non-linear if $g(x)/x$ takes on at least two distinct values as x ranges over B.

8. OTHER CRITERIA FOR LINEARITY GENERATING SETS

Many mathematicians have become interested in the problem of deciding how pathological the behavior of a non-linear additive function must be, or, what is the same question, how light an assumption will imply that an additive function is linear. For example, the pathology of Section 3 led to the sufficient conditions of Section 4.

Some very simple criteria may be phrased in terms of the idea of generating set. If A and B are sets of numbers, let $A - B$ be the set of all differences $x - y$, x in A, y in B. We shall call a set A a *generating set* if $A - A$ contains an interval (of positive length). We shall first see the relevance of this concept, and then study some examples.

Theorem 12.   *If f is additive and bounded on some generating set, f is linear.*

Suppose that $A - A$ contains an interval I, and f is bounded on A, say $|f(x)| < M$ for all x in A. Then for any x in I we have $x = u - v$ for some u, v in A. Then $|f(x)| = |f(u) - f(v)| \leqslant |f(u)| + |f(v)| < 2M$ so that f is bounded on I. The result follows by Theorem 5.

Corollary 4.   *If an additive function is bounded on the set of all irrational numbers between 0 and 1, it is linear.*

This follows from Theorem 12, when we show that every number x between 0 and $1/2$ is the difference of two irrational numbers, each between 0 and 1. If x is irrational, we have $x = 2x - x$, while if x is rational,

$$x = (x + \sqrt{2}/3) - \sqrt{2}/3.$$

EXAMPLE 1:   An interesting set is the set of all numbers between 0 and 1 whose decimal expansion does not use the digit 2. Every number between 0 and 1 can be written as the difference of two such, for example, $0.325 = 0.335 - 0.01$, $0.793 = 0.794 - 0.001$, $0.99 = 0.991 - 0.001$. (A formal proof can easily be constructed.)

EXAMPLE 2:   *The Cantor set is generating.* This result is due to H. Steinhaus. References to four proofs may be found in [3]. (Example 1 is related to this, of course.)

EXAMPLE 3:   Let f be additive and not identically 0. Let A be the set $\{x : f(x) > 0\}$, and let $B = \{x : 0 < f(x) \leqslant 1\}$. Then A is generating, for if t is an arbitrary real number, there exists x such that $f(x) > 0$ and $f(x) > f(t)$. (This follows either from Theorem 1 or Theorem 4.) Then $x - t$ is in A, and $t = x - (x - t)$ is in $A - A$. On the other hand, if f is not linear, B cannot be generating, by Theorem 12.

REMARK 1: Example 3 shows that in Theorem 12 it is not sufficient that f be bounded above or bounded below on a generating set. In Corollary 4, however, "bounded" could be replaced by "bounded above or below." For, by a translation, we know that f is, say, bounded above on S, the set of irrational numbers in $[-1/2, 1/2]$. But $S = -S$, so f is also bounded below on S.

EXAMPLE 4: Let f be additive and $f(1) = 1$. Let $B_n = n + B$, where B is as in Example 3. Then the sequence $\{B_n\}$ is pairwise disjoint (indeed, $B_n = \{x : n < f(x) \leqslant n + 1\}$),

$$R = \bigcup_{-\infty}^{\infty} B_n,$$

and each B_n is a translate of B. Moreover, if f is not linear, no B_n is generating, by Theorem 12.

EXAMPLE 5: No proper subgroup S of the additive group of the reals may be generating. This is because $S = S - S$, and if S contained an interval, we would have, by a translation, $(-\varepsilon, \varepsilon) \subset S$ for some $\varepsilon > 0$. Then

$$R = \bigcup_{\infty}^{\infty} n(-\varepsilon, \varepsilon) \subset S.$$

$\triangle$*Theorem* 13. (Steinhaus [25]) *Every set of positive Lebesgue measure is generating.*

PROOF: (Kestelman [18]) Every set of positive measure includes a closed set of positive measure (simply enclose the complement in an open set of suitably small measure). Thus we may restrict ourselves to a closed bounded set S. Let G be an open set with $G \supset S$, $|G| < 2|S|$ (here $|G|$ stands for the measure of G).

Let δ be the distance, surely positive, between S and the complement of G. The proof will be complete when we show that $S - S$ includes every x with $|x| < \delta$. Now to show that x belongs to $S - S$ it is sufficient to show that $S - x$ meets S, for if $y\varepsilon(S - x) \cap S$, we have $y\varepsilon S$ and $x + y\varepsilon S$ so $x\varepsilon S - y \subset S - S$. To show that $S - x$ meets S we show that $|(S - x) \cap S| > 0$ as follows:

$$|(S - x) \cap S| = |S - x| + |S| - |(S - x) \cup S|$$

$$= 2|S| - |(S - x) \cup S| \geqslant 2|S| - |G| > 0$$

since $S - x \subset G$ by choice of x, and $S \subset G$.

$\triangle$ REMARK: Examples 1 and 2 show that a generating set may have measure zero.

We have now proved the following theorem of Ostrowski [20].

$\triangle$ *Theorem* 14.   *If an additive function is bounded on a set of positive measure, it is linear.*
This follows from Theorems 12 and 13.

$\triangle$ *Corollary* 4.   (Sierpinski [24]) *If f is additive and there exists a measurable function g such that $|f(x)| \leqslant g(x)$ for all x, then f is linear.*
For f is bounded on any set of the form $\{x : g(x) < M\}$. For sufficiently large M, this set has positive measure.

$\triangle$ *Corollary* 5.   (Frechet [7]) *A measurable additive function is linear.*
Another proof is given in Section 11.

$\triangle$ REMARK 2:   In contrast with Theorem 13, a set of second category in R need not be generating. By Example 5, it is sufficient to give a proper subgroup which is of the second category. The procedure of [27], Section 7.5, Problem 18, may be used. See [17], Theorem 10.5 where it is shown that the condition of

Baire forces a second category set to be generating; subsequent theorems yield continuity of additive functions as in Theorem 12 above. See also [1], pp. 78-79 for conditions framed in terms of Baire measurability of functions. For R, these results are a special case of Theorem 14 and its corollaries.

$\triangle$ REMARK 3: The proof of Theorem 13 shows that any set with positive inner measure is generating. Hence Theorem 14 is extended to such sets. A set of positive exterior measure need not be generating, for example, the set B in Example 3. It is not measurable by Theorem 14.

$\triangle$ REMARK 4: The procedure of Remark 1 can be used to strengthen Theorem 14 to one-sided boundedness. This is the form of the result given by Ostrowski.

9. NICE POSSIBILITIES FOR NON-LINEAR FUNCTIONS

This section shows that an additive function may have some nice properties without being linear. Thus, limitations are placed on the program of Sections 4 and 8.

EXAMPLE 6: *An additive non-linear function which is one-to-one and onto the real numbers.* (Thus it is an automorphism of the additive group of the reals. See also Example 9.) Let B be a Hamel basis, and fix v in B. By Theorem 10, there exists an additive function f with $f(v) = v$, $f(b) = 2b$ for all other b in B. Then f is not linear since $f(v)/v \neq f(b)/b$. Now let g be an additive function with $g(v) = v$, $g(b) = b/2$ for all other b in B. For any real x, $x = \alpha v + w$, where α is a rational number and w is a finite rational combination of members of B other than v. Then

$$g[f(x)] = g[\alpha v + 2w] = \alpha g(v) + 2g(w) = \alpha v + w = x,$$

by Theorem 2; similarly $f[g(x)] = x$. Thus $g = f^{-1}$ and so f, having an inverse function, is one-to-one and onto.

$\triangle$ REMARK: Example 6 can be used to give R a topology, different from the usual one, for which addition is continuous, namely the metric $d(x, y) = |f(x) - f(y)|$.

EXAMPLE 7: (Halperin [10]) *An additive non-linear function with the Darboux property.* By definition, such a function has the property that if $f(a) < y < f(b)$, then there exists x between a and b such that $y = f(x)$. Let B be a Hamel basis and fix v in B. Since B is infinite, there exists a mapping from $\{b \varepsilon B : b \neq v\}$ onto B. (It can be a one-to-one correspondence, but this does not concern us.) We shall also define the map at v by mapping v into 0. By Theorem 10 this mapping can be extended to an additive function f. We shall show that for any interval I, $f[I] = R$, the set of all real numbers; this obviously implies the Darboux property. Let y be any real number; then

$$y = \sum_{i=1}^{n} r_i b_i. \qquad \text{Let } x = \sum_{i=1}^{n} r_i f^{-1}(b_i) + av,$$

where a is a rational number chosen so that x will lie in I. Then

$$f(x) = \sum r_i b_i = y,$$

by Theorem 2.

EXAMPLE 8: *An additive non-linear function which takes on only rational values.* If an additive function has only rational values on a Hamel basis B, then it will have only rational values, since every real number is a rational combination of B. The construction of Section 7 can easily be adapted.

EXAMPLE 9: *An additive non-linear function f which satisfies $f[f(x)] = -x$ for all x.* The interest of this result is that if f is linear, say $f(x) = kx$, then $f[f(x)] = k^2 x \neq -x$. Since $-f = f^{-1}$, we also have another instance of Example 6. [$\triangle$ A function with the property given here may be used to set up a complex structure on a real space; namely, one attempts to define ix by taking it to be $f(x)$. See [27], Section 2.11, Problems 6, 7, 8; [5].]

Let B be a Hamel basis and write $B = B_1 \cup B_2$, where B_1, B_2 are disjoint subsets of equal cardinality. Let $T : B_1 \to B_2$ be one-to-one and onto. By Theorem 10, there exists an additive function f with $f(x) = T(x)$ for $x \varepsilon B_1$,

$$f(x) = -T^{-1}(x)$$

for $x \varepsilon B_2$. Then for $x \varepsilon B_1$,

$$f[f(x)] = -T^{-1}[T(x)] = -x,$$

while for $x \varepsilon B_2$,

$$f[f(x)] = f[-T^{-1}(x)] = -f[T^{-1}(x)]$$
$$= -T[T^{-1}(x)] = -x.$$

Thus the required condition is satisfied for all x in B, hence for all real x. [The reader may be interested to check that $f(1)$ is irrational, and that $f(x)$ is rational if and only if x is a rational multiple of $f(1)$.]

EXAMPLE 10: (F. B. Jones) *An additive non-linear function with connected graph.* We omit the construction. See [14], p. 118. Indeed such a function f may have the additional property that $f(x) = 0$ if and only if x is rational. See [14], p. 479. (Of course, Example 8 gives a function whose graph is not connected.) Many pathological properties of the graph are given in [14], where it is seen to provide a unified source of counter-examples.

An additional interesting property of this graph is that it is the union of two relatively closed congruent totally disconnected subsets. See [13].

△ 10. PROPERTIES OF A HAMEL BASIS

A Hamel basis for R must be uncountable since the set of finite rational combinations of a countable set is countable. The interior measure of a basis must be 0, [23], Theorem 1; hence any measurable basis has measure 0, and there do exist measurable bases; indeed every generating set includes one, and we have seen a generating set of measure 0 in Section 8, Example 1. There also exist non-measurable bases; no basis can be Borel measurable, or analytic; but a basis may contain a perfect subset. For these and other similar facts see [23], p. 108, p. 110, p. 234; [14], p. 476, p. 477; and [6].

We have seen in Section 8, Example 4, how a non-linear additive function may be used to obtain pathological decompositions of R. The sets B_n all have zero inner measure, by Section 8, Remark 3, and are pairwise disjoint; yet R is a countable union of them. Other such decompositions may be found in [9].

11. GENERALIZATIONS AND VARIATIONS

A function f is called *subadditive* if

$$f(x+y) \leqslant f(x) + f(y)$$

for all x, y; and *midpoint convex* if

$$f\left(\frac{x+y}{2}\right) \leqslant \tfrac{1}{2}[f(x) + f(y)]$$

for all x, y. Any additive function has both of these properties, and it is interesting to ask which of the theorems proved above can be extended. For example, Corollary 5 (with "linear" replaced by "continuous") is true for midpoint convex functions, [23], Theorem 2; however, no such result can be proved for subadditive functions, as the following result shows.

Theorem 15. *Let g be a bounded function, say $|g(x)| \leqslant M$ for all x. Let $f(x) = 3M + g(x)$. Then f is subadditive.*

For any x, y we have

$$f(x) + f(y) - f(x+y) = 3M + g(x) + g(y) - g(x+y)$$

$$\geqslant 3M - |g(x)| - |g(y)| - |g(x+y)| \geqslant 0.$$

Thus a subadditive function may be bounded and discontinuous, measurable or non-measurable, etc. There is, however, the following easy continuity result which is analogous to Theorem 3.

Theorem 16. *Let f be subadditive with $f(0) = 0$, and assume that f is continuous at 0. Then f is continuous everywhere.*

For any x, y we have

$$f(y) = f(x + y - x) \leqslant f(x) + f(y - x).$$

Thus

$$f(y) - f(x) \leqslant f(y - x).$$

After interchanging x, y, we have

$$|f(x) - f(y)| \leqslant \max |f(x - y), f(y - x)|$$

from which the result follows.

The reader may easily check that an odd subadditive function is additive. For various other results on subadditive functions see [27], Section 2.4, Problems 25–32; Section 10.5, Problems 1–3; also [21].

Subadditive functions play a role in semigroup theory. This may be seen in [12], from which we sketch the following development. It is first shown (Theorem 7.4.1) that a measurable subadditive function is bounded on any closed interval. (An elegant generalization has been given by L. J. Wallen, [26].) Then (Theorem 7.6.1),

$$\lim_{t \to +\infty} f(t)/t$$

is shown to exist and equal $\inf f(t)/t$. From this we obtain another proof of Corollary 5; if f is additive, both f and $-f$ are subadditive; hence

$$\inf f(t)/t = \lim f(t)/t = -\lim[-f(t)/t] = -\inf[-f(t)/t]$$

$$= \sup[f(t)/t].$$

Thus $f(t)/t$ is constant.

A variation of additivity is the discussion of functions of number theoretic type, for example, functions obeying certain laws for integer values of the argument, or for relatively prime pairs of values.

We begin with the remark that if $f(nx) = nf(x)$ for all integer n and all x, the argument used to prove Theorem 2 yields (2) for all rational x, and that if f is monotone this is sufficient to prove (2) for all x. Thus:

Theorem 17.   *Let f be a monotone function satisfying $f(nx) = nf(x)$ for all integer n and all x. Then f is linear.*

This result improves part of Theorem 5 since we did not need to assume that f is additive. See [19] for results of this nature.

An additive arithmetic function f is one such that $f(mn) = f(m) + f(n)$ whenever m, n are relatively prime integers. If f is such a function and $f(n) \leqslant f(n+1)$ for all integer n, then there exists k such that $f(n) = k \log n$. See [22] for a history of this result of P. Erdös. (Compare Section 4, Remark 4.)

A related concept is that of convexity. The reader is referred to [2] and [8] for extensive discussions and bibliography.

APPENDIX. PROOF OF THEOREM 4

Let $k = f(1)$ and choose t so that $f(t) \neq kt$. The graph of f contains all points of the form $[u + vt, uk + vf(t)]$, u, v rational. Let A be the matrix

$$\begin{pmatrix} 1 & k \\ t & f(t) \end{pmatrix}.$$

Then A is non-singular, hence a homeomorphism of the plane onto itself. In particular A preserves dense sets; one dense set is $\{(u, v) : (u, v) \text{ rational}\}$ and A maps this set [via multiplication, XA, where $X = (u, v)$], onto the subset of the graph of f mentioned above. Thus the graph of f is dense.

BIBLIOGRAPHY

[1] S. Banach, *Theorie des opérations linéaires*, Warsaw, 1932.

[2] E. F. Beckenbach, "Convex functions," *Bulletin of the American Mathematical Society* 54(1948): 439–460.

[3] N. C. Bose Majumber, "On the distance set of the Cantor middle third set, III," *American Mathematical Monthly* 72(1965): 725–729.

[4] S. W. Dharmadhikari, "On the functional equation $f(x + y) = f(x) \cdot f(y)$," *American Mathematical Monthly* 72(1965): 847–851.

[5] J. Dieudonné, "Complex structures on real Banach spaces," *Proceedings of the American Mathematical Society* 3(1952): 162–164.

[6] P. Erdös, "On some properties of Hamel bases," *Colloquium Mathematicum* 10(1963): 267–269.

[7] M. Frechet, "Pri la funkcia ekvacio $f(x + y) = f(x) + f(y)$," *Enseignemènt Mathematique* 15(1913): 390–393.

[8] J. W. Green and W. Gustin, "Quasiconvex sets," *Canadian Journal of Mathematics* 2(1950): 489–507.

[9] I. Halperin, "Non-measurable sets and the equation $f(x + y) = f(x) + f(y)$," *Proceedings of the American Mathematical Society* 2(1951): 221–224.

[10] I. Halperin, "Discontinuous functions with the Darboux property," *American Mathematical Monthly* 57(1950): 539–540.

[11] I. N. Herstein, *Topics in Algebra*, Blaisdell, Boston, 1964.

[12] E. Hille and R. S. Phillips, "Functional analysis and semigroups," *American Mathematical Society Colloquium Publications*, vol. 31, 1957.

[13] F. B. Jones, "Solution of #5242," *American Mathematical Monthly*, 72(1965): 1039.

[14] F. B. Jones, "Connected and disconnected plane sets and the functional equation $f(x + y) = f(x) + f(y)$. Measure and other properties of a Hamel basis," *Bulletin of the American Mathematical Society* 48(1942): 115–120, 472–481.

[15] E. Kamke, "Zur Definition der affinen Abbildung," *Jahresbericht der Deutschen Mathematischer-Vereinigung* 36(1927): 145–156.

[16] J. L. Kelley, *General Topology*, Van Nostrand, Princeton, N. J., 1955.

[17] J. L. Kelley and I. Namioka, *Linear Topological Spaces*, Van Nostrand, Princeton, N.J., 1963.

[18] H. Kestelman, "On the functional equation $f(x + y) = f(x) + f(y)$," *Fundamenta Mathematica* 34(1947): 144–147.

[19] J. Milkman, "Note on the functional equations $f(xy) = f(x) + f(y)$, $f(x^n) = nf(x)$," *Proceedings of the American Mathematical Society* 1(1950): 505–508.

[20] A. Ostrowski, "Über die Funktionalgleichung der Exponential-funktion und verwandte Funktionalgleichungen," *Jahresbericht der Deutschen Mathematischer-Vereinigung* 38(1929): 54–62.

[21] S. P. S. Rathore, "On subadditive and superadditive functions," *American Mathematical Monthly* 72(1965): 653–654.

[22] S. L. Segal, "Reviews #3321, 3323," *Mathematical Reviews* 30(1965): 629–630

[23] W. Sierpinski, "Sur la question de la mésurabilité de la base de M. Hamel. Sur les fonctions convexes mésurables," *Fundamenta Mathematica* 1(1920): 105–111, 125–128, 233–235.

[24] W. Sierpinski, "Sur un propriété des fonctions de M. Hamel," *Fundamenta Mathematica* 5(1924): 334–336.

[25] H. Steinhaus, "Sur les distances des points dans les ensembles de mesure positive," *Fundamenta Mathematica* 1(1920): 93–104.

[26] L. J. Wallen, "Problem 4879," *American Mathematical Monthly* 68(1961): 72.

[27] A. Wilansky, *Functional Analysis*, Blaisdell, Boston, 1964.

[28] J. Aczel, "Some unsolved problems in the theory of functional equations," *Archiv der Mathematik* 15 (1964): 435–444.

[29] R. B. Darst, "Measure and other properties of a Hamel basis," *Proceedings of the American Mathematical Society* 16(1965): 645–646.

[30] W. B. Jurkat, "On Cauchy's functional equation," *Proceedings of the American Mathematical Society* 16(1965): 683–686.

[31] S. Kurepa, "The Cauchy functional equation and scalar products in vector spaces," *Mathematical Reviews* 30(1965): 1331.

[32] D. J. Newman, "Problem 4509," *American Mathematical Monthly* 61(1954): 128.

[33]   J. Ratz, "Zur Theorie der Funktionalgleichung $f(xy) = f(x) + f(y)$," *Elemente der Mathematik* 21(1966): 10–13.

[34]   Problems E 1735 (W. Emerson) and 5254 (A. M. Gleason), *American Mathematical Monthly* 72(1965): 912; 73(1966): 93.

ADDITIONAL BIBLIOGRAPHICAL REMARKS

In [28], there is a discussion of several functional equations, and several problems are posed, some of which are solved in [30], [31]. One of these is to show that an additive function satisfying $f(x) = x^2 f(1/x)$ must be linear. This is accomplished by some manipulations beginning with the identity

$$\frac{1}{x(x-1)} = \frac{1}{x-1} - \frac{1}{x}.$$

In [29], results are given which are related to those of [14]. A neat elementary proof of Theorem 14 is given in [33]; and a number theoretic result of the type discussed in Section 11 is given in [34], namely if $f(mn) = f(m)f(n)$ for relatively prime m, n and f is increasing, then f has the form n^k, for some k. See [32] for a similar result.

The result of Remark 4 of Section 4 is also given on p. 404 of E. Hewitt and K. A. Ross, *Abstract Harmonic Analysis*, Academic Press, New York, 1963.

7

Manipulations with Differentials

Made Respectable

M. EVANS MUNROE

UNIVERSITY OF NEW HAMPSHIRE

Professor M. Evans Munroe was born in Georgia, earned his Bachelor's Degree at the University of Texas, and completed his Doctorate at Brown University in 1945. After teaching at Brown and the University of Illinois, he assumed his present position as Professor and Chairman of the Department of Mathematics at the University of New Hampshire in 1959. His interests include integration theory, probability, measure theory, function theory, and the modernization of calculus. His interest in the reduction of differentiable manifold theory to an elementary level is reflected in two textbooks: *Modern Multi-Dimensional Calculus* and *Introductory Real Analysis*.

In the following lecture Professor Munroe shows how the technical advantages of the differential and logical clarity may both be saved by bringing to bear modern theories of multi-dimensional analysis.

MANIPULATIONS WITH DIFFERENTIALS
MADE RESPECTABLE

M. Evans Munroe

An alternative title for this lecture is "The Dilemma of the Conscientious Mathematician Who Wants to Teach Engineering Calculus." With this in mind, we introduce a fictitious character of mixed Welsh and Czech extraction named Cmwwttec. He is, of course, the abbreviation for "Conscientious mathematician who ...."

Cmwwttec's dilemma is that as a mathematician he wants to give an honest presentation of calculus, while as a teacher he wants to give his students as many tools as possible for working with the subject easily. The differential is one of the most efficient working tools in manipulational calculus, and Cmwwttec would like to encourage his students to use this device freely. There are many manipulations with differentials that are easy to learn and that get results (correct ones!) with magical efficiency. Cmwwttec feels that students should not be forced to get results the hard way if there is an easy way; so he wants to present these procedures in his calculus classes and encourage his students to use them.

His office mate is a cynic who says, "You might as well teach calculus that way because as soon as they go across campus to the engineering building that is what they are going to learn anyway."

Nevertheless, Cmwwttec wants to see an honest development for engineering calculus methods before he advocates their unrestricted use.

In order to define the problem a little more precisely, let us look at a few examples.

EXAMPLE 1: In a thermodynamics problem we are given four quantities: p, pressure, v, volume, t, temperature, u, internal energy. The system has two degrees of freedom, and it is frequently required to derive various chain rules connecting various partial derivatives generated by these four quantities. For instance, we might want

$$\left(\frac{\partial p}{\partial v}\right)_t$$

in terms of

$$\left(\frac{\partial p}{\partial v}\right)_u$$

and other appropriate partial derivatives. An easy way to get this is to expand dp in two ways:

$$\left(\frac{\partial p}{\partial v}\right)_t dv + \left(\frac{\partial p}{\partial t}\right)_v dt = dp = \left(\frac{\partial p}{\partial v}\right)_u dv + \left(\frac{\partial p}{\partial u}\right)_v du.$$

Now, on the right, we substitute

$$du = \left(\frac{\partial u}{\partial v}\right)_t dv + \left(\frac{\partial u}{\partial t}\right)_v dt$$

to get

$$\left(\frac{\partial p}{\partial v}\right)_t dv + \left(\frac{\partial p}{\partial t}\right)_v dt = \left(\frac{\partial p}{\partial v}\right)_u dv + \left(\frac{\partial p}{\partial u}\right)_v \left[\left(\frac{\partial u}{\partial v}\right)_t dv + \left(\frac{\partial u}{\partial t}\right)_v dt\right].$$

Since this is an identity in dv and dt, we can set $dv = 1$, $dt = 0$ to obtain the desired chain rule:

$$\left(\frac{\partial p}{\partial v}\right)_t = \left(\frac{\partial p}{\partial v}\right)_u + \left(\frac{\partial p}{\partial u}\right)_v \left(\frac{\partial u}{\partial v}\right)_t.$$

Is this a rigorous derivation of this formula?

EXAMPLE 2: It is immediately apparent from Figure 7.1 that

$$\tan \psi = r \frac{d\theta}{dr}.$$

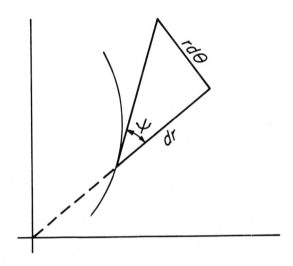

FIG. 7-1

Can this be made a legitimate device for deriving such relations?

EXAMPLE 3: Given an implicit relation such as

$$x^2 + y^2 = 1,$$

to find the derivative of y with respect to x, we take differentials:

$$2x \, dx + 2y \, dy = 0.$$

Then, we solve for dy/dx:

$$\frac{dy}{dx} = \frac{-x}{y}.$$

Is this a legitimate derivation of this result?

EXAMPLE 4:   In order to compute

$$\int_0^1 \sqrt{1 - x^2}\, dx,$$

we "substitute"

$$x = \sin \theta, \qquad dx = \cos \theta\, d\theta$$

to obtain

$$\int_0^{\pi/2} \cos^2 \theta\, d\theta.$$

Is this really substitution or just a device to remember what the right answer is?

EXAMPLE 5:   How do you "substitute" in a multiple integral to get

$$\iint_R f(x, y)\, dx\, dy = \iint_R f[\phi(u, v), \psi(u, v)] \begin{vmatrix} \dfrac{\partial x}{\partial u} & \dfrac{\partial x}{\partial v} \\ \dfrac{\partial y}{\partial u} & \dfrac{\partial y}{\partial v} \end{vmatrix} du\, dv?$$

In general, what do the differentials mean in the notation for an integral?

The real crux of the matter appears in the first step in Example 1. When we equate two different expansions of dp, we are tacitly assuming that "differential of pressure" means something. The symbol p in Example 1 stands for a mapping which associates with each state of the thermodynamic system a numerical measurement of pressure. Mappings of this type are the real object of study in calculus, but far too often they are not properly recognized. Indeed, mathematicians have not bothered to give them a generic name. For purposes of the present discussion, let us call them *physical variables*.

The thermodynamics problem exhibits a typical structure for a calculus problem. It is assumed there that functions f and g exist such that

$$f(v, t) = p = g(v, u),$$

but the functions f and g do not appear in the discussion at all. In general, calculus problems seem to deal with situations in which physical variables are related by what we will call *connecting functions*. The real objects of study are the physical variables; and while the connecting functions sometimes appear specifically, often they are merely understood.

Now the only easy, yet respectable, definition of a differential yields differentials of connecting functions, not of physical variables. Following this theory, we get df and dg in the thermodynamics problem, whereas what Cmwwttec wants is dp. Of course, it is possible to get a sort of dp from df and dg by proving a theorem on invariance under coordinate transformations. However, this approach defeats Cmwwttec's whole purpose because in the proof of the invariance theorem you have to use the very chain rule he is trying to derive.

Looking back now through all the examples given above, we get the following picture of Cmwwttec's dream world. It is a world in which:

1.   Physical variables have their own intrinsically defined differentials. Specifically, if u is a physical variable, du is defined in terms of u alone without reference to any other differentials or to any connecting functions.

2.   The usual linear relations among differentials, with derivatives for coefficients, are provable from this definition.

3.   Derivatives can be expressed as genuine quotients of differentials.

4.   Differential triangles, such as the one shown in Figure 7-1, picture differentials exactly and so may be used to derive results of geometric significance.

5.   The differential that appears in an integral is the same as that used in differential calculus, and a change of variable in an integral (either single or multiple) is accomplished by a genuine substitution process.

We now turn to the project of constructing Cmwwttec's dream world for him. The major hurdle is to obtain his item 1.

Once this is properly done, the other items fall into place very easily.

To begin with, let us look at one-dimensional calculus. By this we mean the following. We consider a collection of physical variables all defined on some common domain which, for convenience, we will represent as a curve C in the plane. For example, suppose a particle is moving on the curve C. Pertinent physical variables would be:

x, the mapping which carries each position of the particle into the abscissa of that position

y, the ordinate mapping

s, the mapping that carries each particle position into its distance along C from some fixed reference point

t, the mapping that gives the time for each particle position.

Components of velocity and acceleration furnish other physical variables, and there might be many more. In any case, the general picture is that of a set of physical variables defined on C. The thing that determines dimension is the nature of the connecting functions. In a one-dimensional problem the physical variables are connected by relations of the form

$$v = f(u).$$

This means that the mapping v is identically equal to the composite mapping u followed by f. In a two-dimensional problem the relations assume the form

$$w = f(u, v).$$

It is possible to describe postulationally the type of structure on which the modern definition of differential is based, but we shall not be that precise here. It suffices to say that we are going to talk about a set of physical variables defined on a curve C, and we shall assume that there is one of these variables u such that for every other variable v in the problem we have a function f with continuous third derivative such that

$$v = f(u).$$

The differential of one of these physical variables will be a mapping whose domain is the family of tangent lines to C. That is, a value of dv will be written $dv(p, q)$ where p and q are as shown in Figure 7-2. Differentials are defined on point pairs (p, q) where

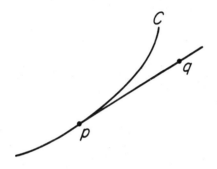

Fig. 7-2

p is on C and q is on the tangent line to C at p.

Recall now that dv is to be generated by v alone. But, how can v, which is defined only on C, generate something that operates on points q which are not on C? The extremely ingenious answer to this question involves representing the tangent line (a one-dimensional linear space) by an abstract one-dimensional linear space whose elements are things that operate on variables like v.

Specifically, we shall represent the tangent line by what are called derivative operators. First, look at an example. A differentiable function f (from real numbers to real numbers) determines, through the usual limit of a difference quotient procedure, another function f'. Now, suppose u and v are physical variables and that

$$v = f(u).$$

We define a new physical variable $D_u v$, called the derivative of v with respect to u, by setting

$$D_u v = f'(u).$$

We now think of D_u as a mapping that carries one physical variable into another,

$$D_u : v \to D_u v.$$

This mapping D_u is an example of a derivative operator.

More generally, we define derivative operators postulationally. An operator D which maps physical variables on C into other physical variables on C is called a derivative operator at a point p of C, provided that for any constants a and b and any physical variables u and v

$$(i)\ \ D(au + bv)(p) = aDu(p) + bDv(p),$$

$$(ii)\ \ D(uv)(p) = u(p)Dv(p) + v(p)Du(p).$$

It follows at once from these postulates that D operating on a constant gives 0 because by (i)

$$D(au) = aDu,$$

while by (ii)

$$D(au) = aDu + uDa.$$

Choosing $u \neq 0$, we have $Da = 0$. It is also evident from (ii) that

$$Du^2 = 2uDu.$$

Now suppose that

$$v = f(u),$$

where f is thrice differentiable. There then exists a differentiable function g such that

$$v = v(p) + D_u v(p)[u - u(p)] + g(u)[u - u(p)]^2.$$

We operate on this equation with D at p, where D satisfies the derivative operator postulates. The result is

$$Dv(p) = D_u v(p) Du(p) + D[g(u)](p)[\, u(p) - u(p)]^2$$

$$+ 2g(u)[u(p) - u(p)]Du(p)$$

$$= D_u v(p) Du(p). \tag{1}$$

Let us regard this as an identity in v and p. We are then saying that at each point of C, the operator D has the property that over its entire domain

$$D = Du D_u .$$

Every derivative operator is a multiple of the operator D_u. This is the required result that at each point of C the set of derivative operators has the structure of a one-dimensional linear space.

So, we no longer return to Figure 7-2 and say that we want to define

$$dv(p, q).$$

Instead, we represent the tangent line at p by the set of derivative operators at p and say that we want to define

$$dv(p, D),$$

where D is a derivative operator at p. This is easy.

DEFINITION:

$$dv(p, D) = Dv(p).$$

This achieves fully item 1 in Cmwwttec's dream world; dv is generated by v alone. Substituting this defining equation into Equation (1) above, we have

$$dv(p, D) = D_u v(p) du(p, D)$$

for all p and D, which is to say

$$dv = D_u v \, du$$

over the entire family of tangents. This is Cmwwttec's item 2, and division yields his item 3:

$$\frac{dv}{du} = D_u v.$$

We showed that the set of derivative operators is a linear space and agreed to identify it with the tangent line. There is still one degree of freedom in setting up this identification. In the one-dimensional case we get the usual geometric representation of differentials by letting the operator D_s (derivative with respect to arc length) be the unit vector on the tangent line. Then

$$ds(D_s) = D_s s = 1,$$

and in Figure 7-3

$$dx(D_s) = D_s x = \cos \alpha$$

$$dy(D_s) = D_s y = \sin \alpha.$$

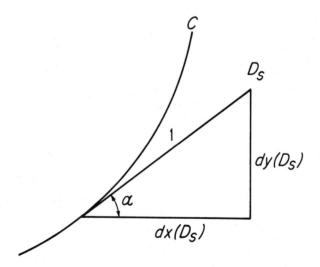

Fig. 7-3

Since the differentials are linear, they have proportional values on other tangent vectors.

Let us turn now to the multi-dimensional cases. Here we have a base set of variables

$$u_1, u_2, \ldots, u_n$$

and consider all physical variables v such that

$$v = f(u_1, u_2, \ldots, u_n), \tag{2}$$

where f has continuous third partial derivatives. The fundamental derivative operators are

$$\frac{\partial}{\partial u_i}.$$

They are defined by saying that, given (2),

$$\frac{\partial v}{\partial u_i} = f_i(u_1, u_2, \ldots, u_n),$$

where f_i denotes the partial derivative of f with respect to its ith argument.

The abstract definition of derivative operator carries over verbatim. Not even the notation needs to be changed. The parallel to Equation (1) above reads

$$Dv(p) = \sum_{i=1}^{n} \frac{\partial v}{\partial u_i}(p) \, Du_i(p). \tag{3}$$

This is derived from an n-dimensional Taylor-like expansion exactly as Equation (1) was. We interpret this relation as saying

$$D = \sum_{i=1}^{n} Du_i \frac{\partial}{\partial u_i},$$

and we see the n-dimensional linear space structure with the operators

$$\frac{\partial}{\partial u_i}$$

as the basis vectors.

We identify the linear space of derivative operators with the tangent n space and have exactly the same definition of differential as before:

$$dv(p,\, D) = Dv(p).$$

Substituting this into (3), we have the basic relation among differentials:

$$dv = \sum_{i=1}^{n} \frac{\partial v}{\partial u_i}\, du_i. \tag{4}$$

The geometric picture depends on the nature of the underlying domain of the physical variables, but it is instructive to look at the two-dimensional case in which this domain is the xy plane. Here the "tangent" plane at p is merely a superposed plane with origin at p. We calibrate the tangent planes by setting the operators

$$\frac{\partial}{\partial x}, \qquad \frac{\partial}{\partial y}$$

equal to unit vectors in the x and y directions, respectively. Since

$$dx\!\left(\frac{\partial}{\partial x}\right) = \frac{\partial x}{\partial x} = 1, \qquad dx\!\left(\frac{\partial}{\partial y}\right) = \frac{\partial x}{\partial y} = 0,$$

$$dy\!\left(\frac{\partial}{\partial x}\right) = \frac{\partial y}{\partial y} = 0, \qquad dy\!\left(\frac{\partial}{\partial y}\right) = \frac{\partial y}{\partial y} = 1,$$

we have the situation pictured in Figure 7-4, and this yields the usual geometric significance for dx and dy.

It is interesting to look at the geometric significance of the polar coordinate differentials. Since

$$\frac{\partial x}{\partial r} = \cos\theta, \qquad \frac{\partial x}{\partial \theta} = r\sin\theta,$$

$$\frac{\partial y}{\partial r} = \sin\theta, \qquad \frac{\partial y}{\partial \theta} = r\cos\theta,$$

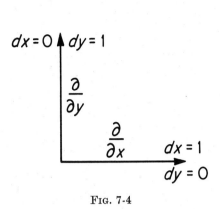

FIG. 7-4

we have from Equation (4) the matrix equation

$$\begin{bmatrix} dx \\ dy \end{bmatrix} = \begin{bmatrix} \cos\theta & -r\sin\theta \\ \sin\theta & r\cos\theta \end{bmatrix} \begin{bmatrix} dr \\ d\theta \end{bmatrix}$$

$$= \begin{bmatrix} \cos\theta & -\sin\theta \\ \sin\theta & \cos\theta \end{bmatrix} \begin{bmatrix} dr \\ r\,d\theta \end{bmatrix}.$$

Thus, the system $(dr, r\,d\theta)$ appears as a rotation of (dx, dy), and Figure 7-1 is put on a firm foundation.

Turning to integrals, we note first that to make sense out of

$$\int_a^b f(x)\,dx$$

we should recognize it as the line integral of a physical variable $f(x)$ over a domain $C = [a, b]$, with respect to a differential dx defined on the family of tangents to C. So, the basic form to study is

$$\int_C u\,dv.$$

This may be defined as follows. Partition C by points $p_0, p_1, \ldots, p_n$ and on the tangent line at p_i determine a point D_i so that

$$\text{dist}(p_i, D_i) = \text{arc}(p_i, p_{i+1}).$$

See Figure 7-5.

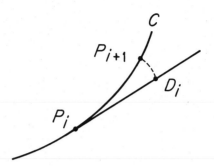

FIG. 7-5

Now, define the integral as follows:

$$\int_C u \, dv = \lim \sum_{i=0}^{n-1} u(p_i) \, dv(p_i, D_i),$$

where the limit is taken as the maximum distance between successive partition points tends to zero.

By contrast, the usual procedure is to use Figure 7-6 in defining

$$\int_C u \, dx$$

and Figure 7-7 in defining

$$\int_C u \, dy.$$

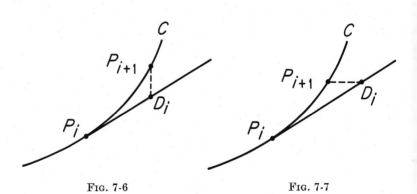

FIG. 7-6   FIG. 7-7

Since in the definition outlined above the D_i depend in no way on the variable v, the approximating sums are invariant under the substitution

$$dv(p_i, D_i) = D_w v(p_i)\, dw(p_i, D_i)$$

and obviously

$$\int_C u\, dv = \int_C u\, D_w v\, dw.$$

For the double integral case we need a product of differentials operating on plane areas. This is the so-called exterior product, and the clue to defining it lies in Figure 7-8.

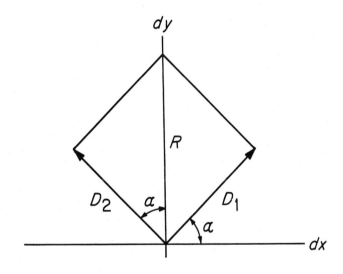

FIG. 7-8

From this figure we have

$$dx(D_1) = |D_1|\, \cos \alpha,$$

$$dy(D_1) = |D_1|\, \sin \alpha,$$

$$dx(D_2) = -|D_2|\, \sin \alpha,$$

$$dy(D_2) = |D_2|\, \cos \alpha;$$

so

$$\begin{vmatrix} dx(D_1) & dx(D_2) \\ dy(D_1) & dy(D_2) \end{vmatrix} = \begin{vmatrix} |D_1| \cos \alpha & |D_2| \sin \alpha \\ -|D_1| \sin \alpha & |D_2| \cos \alpha \end{vmatrix}$$

$$= |D_1| \, |D_2| = \text{area } (R).$$

Thus, a measure on rectangles that is a generalization of area is furnished by

$$du \wedge dv(R) = \begin{vmatrix} du(D_1) & du(D_2) \\ dv(D_1) & dv(D_2) \end{vmatrix},$$

where u and v are any physical variables on the plane and R is generated by the vectors D_1 and D_2.

It is readily verified that the exterior multiplication, denoted here by $\wedge$, has the following properties:

$$du \wedge dv = -dv \wedge du,$$

$$du \wedge du = 0,$$

$$du \wedge (a \, dv + b \, dw) = a \, du \wedge dv + b \, du \wedge dw.$$

Using these rules of manipulation, we find that

$$dx \wedge dy = \left(\frac{\partial x}{\partial u} \, du + \frac{\partial x}{\partial v} \, dv \right) \wedge \left(\frac{\partial y}{\partial u} \, du + \frac{\partial y}{\partial v} \, dv \right),$$

$$= \begin{vmatrix} \dfrac{\partial x}{\partial u} & \dfrac{\partial x}{\partial v} \\ \dfrac{\partial y}{\partial u} & \dfrac{\partial y}{\partial v} \end{vmatrix} du \wedge dv. \tag{5}$$

From this we get a genuine substitution theorem for double integrals if only we define the approximating sums on a structure that is independent of the variables to appear in the integrals. A simple way to do this is to cross-hatch a region R into rectangles R_i no matter what variables are going to appear. For example, to define an integral in r and θ we do not have to turn to Figure 7-9 because $dr \wedge d\theta$ applies to rectangles as well as $dx \wedge dy$ does.

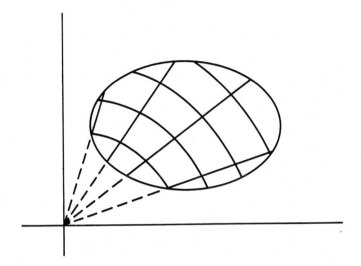

Fig. 7-9

So, we define

$$\iint_R w \, du \wedge dv = \lim \sum w(p_i) \, du \wedge dv_{p_i}(R_i),$$

where p_i is a point of the rectangle R_i. Clearly,

$$\iint_R w \, dx \wedge dy = \iint_R w \begin{vmatrix} \dfrac{\partial x}{\partial u} & \dfrac{\partial x}{\partial v} \\ \dfrac{\partial y}{\partial u} & \dfrac{\partial y}{\partial v} \end{vmatrix} du \wedge dv$$

because the substitution (5) does not alter the approximating sums.

So, Cmwwttec's dilemma is resolved. The cynical office mate has commented that the resolution is more painful than the dilemma itself, but Cmwwttec does not feel that way about it. He does wish that the definition of a differential were less sophisticated, but he sees no choice in the matter because in the current state of knowledge anything less sophisticated fails to get the job done.

There does remain some question as to what can be done with this in the presentation of elementary calculus. One effect of this theory can be to instill confidence in the professor himself that manipulative calculus is respectable. Then, at least, he can exhort his students to use such tricks without hating himself after each lecture. Cmwwttec feels that this is not enough. Of course, it is essential for the professor to have confidence, but the student should be given some confidence, too. It probably does not inspire a lot of confidence in the student to tell him, "This is the most effective way to get the results we are interested in, and it can be rigorously justified. However, the justification involves a theory you are too young to be told about."

Rather, Cmwwttec devotes a couple of lectures to the modern definition of a differential. He emphasizes, however, that in order to use differentials effectively it is not necessary to recall the details of the definition. Instead, the rather involved definition is designed to establish three items, and these three items are the springboard from which one starts a fascinating program of using differentials to find all kinds of things. These items are:

1. Each physical variable has its own differential.

2. In an n-dimensional problem differentials satisfy relations of the form

$$dv = \sum_{i=1}^{n} \frac{\partial v}{\partial u_i} \, du_i .$$

3. Differentials measure components of tangent vectors, and the differentials of rectangular coordinates measure components in the coordinate directions.

The definition of a differential summarized here is now a standard part of modern differential geometry. So far, however, mathematicians seem to regard this as classified information available only to graduate students. In essence, this lecture is a plea that this information be released to calculus students because they can really use it in their work.

8

Exterior Differential Calculus and Maxwell's Equations

OSWALD WYLER

CARNEGIE INSTITUTE OF TECHNOLOGY

A native of Switzerland, Professor Oswald Wyler earned
his Diploma in mathematics and physics (1946) and his
Doctorate (1950) from the Swiss Federal Institute of
Technology. After holding research and teaching appoint-
ments at the Institute of Geophysics of the Swiss Federal
Institute of Technology, the University of Chicago,
Northwestern University, and the University of New
Mexico, he came to the Carnegie Institute of Technology
where he is now Professor of Mathematics. His research
interests include foundations of geometry, algebra of
ordinary differential equations, categories of algebraic
structures, and convergence spaces.

Professor Wyler's lecture follows naturally after that
of Professor Munroe. Indeed, this lecture discusses the
algebra and applications of the approach to differentials
whose pedagogical value is supported in the previous
lecture.

EXTERIOR DIFFERENTIAL CALCULUS AND MAXWELL'S EQUATIONS

Oswald Wyler

The aim of this lecture is to demonstrate some techniques of exterior differential calculus, and to apply these to Maxwell's equations of electrodynamics.

1. EXTERIOR DIFFERENTIAL CALCULUS

Exterior differential calculus, introduced about sixty years ago by the great French mathematician Elie Cartan, has been recognized for some time as the natural technique for line and surface integrals, and for their analogs in higher-dimensional spaces. It is at the same time simpler and more general than vector calculus, and it replaces a host of special theorems of vector calculus by a few simple, and easily remembered, rules. Vector calculus is restricted to three-dimensional space; exterior differential calculus operates in spaces of any dimension. Let us see how it works.

Exterior differential calculus is a calculus of differential forms. Briefly, but not very precisely, we may define a *differential form* as something that occurs under an integral sign. In three-dimensional space, this leads to the following possibilities:

$U_x \, dx + U_y \, dy + U_z \, dz$ for line integrals;

$U_x \, dy \, dz + U_y \, dz \, dx + U_z \, dx \, dy$ for surface integrals;

$f \, dx \, dy \, dz$ for volume integrals.

In these expressions, U_x, U_y, U_z represent components of a vector field $\mathbf{U}$, and f represents a scalar field. In vector calculus, the first two integrands are often written as $U_t \, ds$ and $U_n \, d\sigma$, where U_t and U_n are tangential and normal components of $\mathbf{U}$, and ds and $d\sigma$ denote a "line element" and a "surface element."

The formal expressions written above are *differential forms*, of *order* 1, 2, 3, respectively. It will be very useful to regard a scalar field f as a differential form too, of order 0. Thus exterior differential calculus replaces vector fields, and also scalar fields, by differential forms.

Differential forms can be added and multiplied. We add any two differential forms *of the same order* according to the rules of ordinary algebra. This obviously corresponds to the addition of vectors and of vector fields.

Before discussing the multiplication of differential forms, let us look quickly at some familiar integrals. The integral $\int_a^b f(x) \, dx$ is known as an *oriented* integral. If we reverse orientation, that is if we consider $\int_b^a f(x) \, dx$, the integral simply changes sign. Now look at a double integral $\iint_A f(x, y) \, dx \, dy$. It is often advantageous to consider this as an oriented integral which changes sign if we change orientation. How do we do this? In the plane, orientation is determined by the order of the coordinate axes: first the x axis, then the y axis. Changing orientation then means to change the order of the coordinate axes. We may indicate this by replacing the expression $f(x, y) \, dx \, dy$ under the integral sign with $f(x, y) \, dy \, dx$. Since changing the orientation should change the sign, we are tempted to write

$$f(x, y) \, dy \, dx = -f(x, y) \, dx \, dy,$$

or just

$$dy\, dx = -dx\, dy. \tag{1}$$

This simple device has far-reaching consequences.

We are ready now to define the multiplication of differential forms. We multiply two differential forms, of the same order or of different orders, by using the rules of ordinary algebra, with one very important exception. When we change the order of two coordinate differentials, we use the basic equation (1) and *change the sign.*

Let me show you by some examples how this works.

If we form the product

$$(U_x\, dx + U_y\, dy + U_z\, dz)(V_x\, dx + V_y\, dy + V_z\, dz),$$

we expect nine terms. One of them would be $U_x\, dx V_x\, dx = U_x V_x\, dx\, dx$. But $dx\, dx = -dx\, dx$ by our basic rule, if we interchange the two factors, and hence $dx\, dx = 0$, so that this term vanishes. Two other terms are $U_x V_y\, dx\, dy$ and $U_y V_x\, dy\, dx = -U_y V_x\, dx\, dy$. Treating the other six terms similarly, we end up with the following result:

$$(U_y V_z - U_z V_y)\, dy\, dz + (U_z V_x - U_x V_z)\, dz\, dx$$
$$+ (U_x V_y - U_y V_x)\, dx\, dy.$$

This looks exactly like the vector product $\mathbf{U} \times \mathbf{V}$.

Let us now consider the product

$$(U_x\, dx + U_y\, dy + U_z\, dz)(V_x\, dy\, dz + V_y\, dz\, dx + V_z\, dx\, dy).$$

We expect again nine terms. But in six of these, coordinate differential factors are repeated, and it follows that they vanish. For instance, $dx\, dz\, dx = -dz\, dx\, dx$ by rule (1). But $dx\, dx = 0$, again by (1), and hence $dx\, dz\, dx = 0$. The remaining three terms have a common factor $dx\, dy\, dz$, and the product is

$$(U_x V_x + U_y V_y + U_z V_z)\, dx\, dy\, dz.$$

This reminds us of the scalar product $\mathbf{U} \cdot \mathbf{V}$.

Apart from products with scalar fields—which we need not discuss—these are the only interesting products of differential forms in three-space. The reason for this is that other products would lead to differential forms of order four or higher, and these do not exist in three-space. More exactly, they vanish. If we multiply four or more factors dx, dy, dz, then at least one factor is repeated, and we have seen that a product of coordinate differentials with repeated factors vanishes.

Let me give you one more example of multiplication of differential forms. Suppose that we want to change variables in an oriented double integral $\iint_A f(x, y)\, dx\, dy$, from x, y to u, v. We put

$$dx = \frac{\partial x}{\partial u}\, du + \frac{\partial x}{\partial v}\, dv, \qquad dy = \frac{\partial y}{\partial u}\, du + \frac{\partial y}{\partial v}\, dv,$$

and we multiply. By the basic rule (1), we have

$$du\, du = dv\, dv = 0, \qquad dv\, du = -du\, dv,$$

and thus we obtain:

$$dx\, dy = \begin{vmatrix} \dfrac{\partial x}{\partial u} & \dfrac{\partial x}{\partial v} \\[2ex] \dfrac{\partial y}{\partial u} & \dfrac{\partial y}{\partial v} \end{vmatrix} du\, dv = \frac{\partial(x, y)}{\partial(u, v)}\, du\, dv.$$

This is exactly what we need.

Now let us look at differentiation. If ω is a differential form of order r, then the *differential* $d\omega$ of ω is, by definition, a differential form of order $r + 1$, obtained by the following three simple rules.

First rule: Differentiation is additive; we differentiate "term by term."

Second rule: The differential of a scalar field, or differential form of order 0, has its usual meaning. For example,

$$du = \frac{\partial u}{\partial x}\, dx + \frac{\partial u}{\partial y}\, dy + \frac{\partial u}{\partial z}\, dz$$

for a scalar field u in three-dimensional space, with coordinates x, y, z.

Third rule: Coordinate differentials are treated as constants. More exactly, $d(\psi\, du) = d\psi\, du$ for a product of a differential form ψ by a coordinate differential du.

EXAMPLE 1: Differentials in three-space. Let me introduce first two convenient abbreviations which I shall use throughout this lecture. If **U** is a vector field with components U_x, U_y, U_z, then I put:

$$[\mathbf{U}]_1 = U_x\, dx + U_y\, dy + U_z\, dz.$$
$$[\mathbf{U}]_2 = U_x\, dy\, dz + U_y\, dz\, dx + U_z\, dx\, dy. \tag{2}$$

With these notations, we have

$$df = [\operatorname{grad} f]_1, \quad d[\mathbf{U}]_1 = [\operatorname{curl} \mathbf{U}]_2, \quad d[\mathbf{U}]_2 = (\operatorname{div} \mathbf{U})\, dx\, dy\, dz, \tag{3}$$

for a scalar field f and a vector field **U** in three-space. Thus exterior differential calculus replaces the three differential operators of vector calculus by one.

EXAMPLE 2: In physics, we deal with four dimensions, one for time and three for space. We define the positive orientation of the physical universe by the order t, x, y, z of coordinate axis directions, where t is time and x, y, z are space coordinates, with the usual right-hand orientation. We have

$$df = [\operatorname{grad} f]_1 + \frac{\partial f}{\partial t}\, dt,$$

$$d([\mathbf{U}]_1 - f\, dt) = [\operatorname{curl} \mathbf{U}]_2 + dt\left[\frac{\partial \mathbf{U}}{\partial t} + \operatorname{grad} f\right]_1,$$

$$d([\mathbf{P}]_2 - dt[\mathbf{U}]_1) = (\operatorname{div} \mathbf{P})\, dx\, dy\, dz + dt\left[\frac{\partial \mathbf{P}}{\partial t} + \operatorname{curl} \mathbf{U}\right]_2, \tag{4}$$

$$d(f\, dx\, dy\, dz - dt[\mathbf{P}]_2) = \left(\frac{\partial f}{\partial t} + \operatorname{div} \mathbf{P}\right) dt\, dx\, dy\, dz,$$

for a scalar field f and vector fields **U** and **P**.

Formulas (3) and (4) follow easily from the three rules given above and the algebra of differential forms. I shall leave their verification to you.

The rules of exterior differential calculus are similar to those of ordinary calculus. For instance, we have the product rule

$$d(\omega\psi) = (d\omega)\psi + (-1)^r \omega(d\psi),$$

where r is the order of the differential form ω. One very important rule has no analog in ordinary calculus. It is

$$d(d\omega) = 0 \tag{5}$$

In our first example, this becomes:

$$\text{curl grad } f = 0, \qquad \text{div curl } \mathbf{U} = 0.$$

Again, one rule replaces several.

2. THE THEOREM OF STOKES

I claimed at the beginning of this lecture that exterior differential calculus is the natural technique for line and surface integrals. If this is so, then we should be able to formulate the integral theorems of vector calculus in terms of differential forms. Actually, we can do much better than that.

We consider a differential form ω of order $r - 1$, defined in and near an r-dimensional region R. For $r = 1$, R is a curve. For $r = 2$, R is a region on a surface. For $r = 3$, R is a volume in three-space–or maybe a three-dimensional region in four-dimensional space. We suppose that R has a well-behaved boundary which we denote by ∂R. If R is a volume in three-space, then ∂R is a closed surface. If R is a region of a surface, or of the plane, then ∂R is a closed curve.

It is important that R and ∂R are oriented, with *matching orientations*. These are obtained as follows. At a regular point p of ∂R, we define the *outward normal* of ∂R as a vector $\mathbf{n}$ at p, perpendicular to ∂R and pointing out of R. If R is a region of a surface (or an arc of a curve), then we require that $\mathbf{n}$ be tangent to that surface (or to the curve). An orientation of ∂R is defined by $r-1$ independent directions $\mathbf{u}_1, \ldots, \mathbf{u}_{r-1}$, in ∂R and at p, in a given order. These directions can be, and often are, determined by a system of curvilinear coordinates $u_1, \ldots, u_{r-1}$ in ∂R. If an orientation $\mathbf{u}_1, \ldots, \mathbf{u}_{r-1}$ of ∂R is given, then the r directions $\mathbf{n}, \mathbf{u}_1, \ldots, \mathbf{u}_{r-1}$, in this order, determine an orientation of R. This is the matching orientation.

If R and ∂R are oriented, with matching orientations, then we have the simple formula

$$\int_R d\omega = \int_{\partial R} \omega \tag{6}$$

This is known as the *generalized theorem of Stokes.*

The generalized theorem of Stokes includes all integral theorems of vector calculus: Green's theorem, the theorem of Stokes for a region on a surface, and the divergence theorem. In fact, all known integral theorems of this type are special cases of the generalized theorem of Stokes.

EXAMPLE 1: The simplest special case of Stokes's theorem is the following. We let R be an interval $a \leqslant x \leqslant b$ (or $a \geqslant x \geqslant b$) of the real line, oriented from a to b. Then the boundary of R, with matching orientation, consists of the point b, positively oriented, and of the point a, negatively oriented. We have $r = 1$, so that ω is of order 0, i.e. a function f. Stokes's theorem for this case is well-known:

$$\int_a^b df = f(b) - f(a).$$

More generally, if C is an oriented arc, in a space of any dimension, with initial point a and end point b, then

$$\int_C df = f(b) - f(a)$$

for any scalar field f defined on (and near) C.

EXAMPLE 2:   We shall need this in discussing Maxwell's equations. Let A be a region on a surface in three-space, with boundary ∂A. Then we have, of course, the ordinary theorem of Stokes:

$$\int_{\partial A} [\mathbf{U}]_1 = \iint_A [\operatorname{curl} \mathbf{U}]_2 .$$

We have also a three-dimensional Stokes's theorem in four-dimensional space, as follows.

We consider the surface region A during a fixed time interval, say for $a \leqslant t \leqslant b$. If we denote the time interval by I, this means that we consider a three-dimensional cylindrical region $I \times A$ in four-dimensional space. How does Stokes's theorem apply to this region?

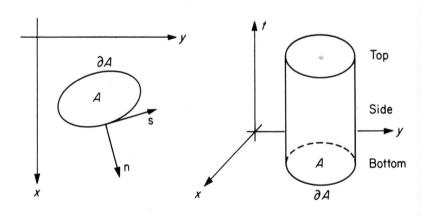

FIG. 8-1

In Figure 8-1, I have drawn A as a region of the (x, y) plane, so that $I \times A$ becomes a cylinder in a three-dimensional space with coordinates t, x, y. However, our discussion will be valid for a region A on any surface in three-space.

We may describe the boundary of $I \times A$ by the formula

$$\partial(I \times A) = (\partial I) \times A - I \times (\partial A).$$

In other terms,

$$\iint_{\partial(I \times A)} \omega = \iint_{(\partial I) \times A} \omega - \iint_{I \times (\partial A)} \omega$$

for a differential form ω of order 2. Let me explain this.

The boundary of $I \times A$ consists of three parts which we may call top, bottom, and side of the cylinder. The top is A at $t = b$, with the given orientation, and the bottom is A at $t = a$, with the opposite orientation. Since ∂I consists of b, positively oriented, and of a, negatively oriented, top and bottom together, with the proper orientations, form $(\partial I) \times A$, and we have

$$\iint_{(\partial I) \times A} \omega = \iint_A \omega \, \Big|_{t=a}^{t=b}$$

for a differential form ω of order 2.

Geometrically, the side of $I \times A$ is $I \times (\partial A)$. If $\mathbf{n}$ is the outer normal of ∂A, and $\mathbf{s}$ a tangent vector of ∂A such that $\mathbf{n}, \mathbf{s}$ defines the given orientation of A, then $\mathbf{s}$ determines the matching orientation of ∂A, and $t, \mathbf{s}$ defines the orientation of $I \times (\partial A)$. But the orientation of $I \times A$ is $t, \mathbf{n}, \mathbf{s}$, or equivalently $\mathbf{n}, \mathbf{s}, t$, so that $\mathbf{s}, t$, and not $t, \mathbf{s}$, is the matching orientation of the side of $I \times A$. Thus $-I \times (\partial A)$, and not $I \times (\partial A)$, is part of $\partial(I \times A)$.

On top and at the bottom of $I \times A$, we have $t = $ const. and hence $dt = 0$. On the side of $I \times A$, the coordinate differentials dx, dy, dz are scalar multiples

$$\frac{dx}{ds} \, ds, \frac{dy}{ds} \, ds, \frac{dz}{ds} \, ds$$

of a single differential ds, where s is a parameter on ∂A. It follows that $dy \, dz = dz \, dx = dx \, dy = 0$ on the side of $I \times A$. Thus we have

$$\iint_{\partial(I \times A)} \omega = \iint_A [\mathbf{P}]_2 \, \Big|_{t=a}^{t=b} + \int_a^b dt \int_{\partial A} [\mathbf{U}]_1, \qquad (7)$$

for a differential form $\omega = [\mathbf{P}]_2 - dt[\mathbf{U}]_1$ of order 2.

In A, and hence in $I \times A$, the differentials dx, dy, dz can be expressed in terms of the differentials du, dv of two surface parameters u, v, and it follows that $dx \, dy \, dz = 0$ in $I \times A$. Thus

$$\iiint_{I \times A} \psi = \int_a^b dt \iint_A [\mathbf{Q}]_2 \tag{8}$$

for a differential form $\psi = f \, dx \, dy \, dz + dt \, [\mathbf{Q}]_2$ of order 3. If $\psi = d\omega$ for $\omega = [\mathbf{P}]_2 - dt[\mathbf{U}]_1$, then $\mathbf{Q} = \partial \mathbf{P}/\partial t + \operatorname{curl} \mathbf{U}$ by (4). Combining this with (7) and (8), we obtain Stokes's theorem for $I \times A$.

Let us look back for a moment at what we have accomplished. We have replaced three products, three differential operators, three integral theorems of vector calculus by one product, one differential operator, one integral theorem for exterior differential calculus. Moreover, the rules of exterior differential calculus are much simpler than those of vector calculus, and they apply not only to three-dimensional spaces, but to spaces of any dimension. This is very useful not only for the mathematician, but also for the physicist and the engineer. As an added bonus, and by no means a small one, we find that the rules for a change of variables in multiple integrals become almost as simple, and as automatic, as the corresponding rules of elementary calculus.

In my presentation of exterior differential calculus, I could, of course, only sketch the main ideas, and I had to leave out almost all details, but fortunately there is a handy reference: *Differential Forms with Applications to the Physical Sciences*, by Harley Flanders (New York, Academic Press, 1963). This rather small book (200 pages) contains a wealth of material in very concise form.

Let me turn now to the second topic of this lecture.

3. MAXWELL'S EQUATIONS

I begin by presenting the physical concepts which enter electrodynamics, and the units in which they are measured.

Electrodynamics have been plagued with at least four quite different systems of measurement, but I cannot discuss them here. I restrict myself to the system in most common use today. Its basic units are the *meter* as unit of length, the *kilogram* as unit of mass, the *second* as unit of time, and the *ampere* as unit of electrical current. All other units are derived from these. I mention only the unit of energy because of its importance: 1 watt sec = 1 volt amp sec = 1 m^2 kg/sec^2.

In electrodynamics, we consider three fields and their interaction. Each of the three fields is usually represented by two component fields. The following table indicates the fields, their component fields, and the letters and units used for them.

Field	Letter	Unit
I. *Electromagnetic intensity*		
(a) Electrical intensity or field strength	**E**	volt/m
(b) Magnetic induction or flux density	**B**	volt sec/m^2
II. *Electromagnetic induction or flux density*		
(a) Magnetic field strength	**H**	amp/m
(b) Electrical displacement or flux density	**D**	amp sec/m^2
III. *Electrical current*		
(a) Electrical current density	**J**	amp/m^2
(b) Electrical charge density	ρ	amp sec/m^3

Of the six component fields, the last one is a scalar field, the others are vector fields. The nomenclature in the table may seem a bit confusing, but this cannot be helped. The magnetic fields were named before their nature was properly understood, and we are stuck with the wrong names.

Maxwell's equations are the basic laws of electrodynamics. You may be familiar with the differential form of these laws:

$$\operatorname{curl} \mathbf{H} = \frac{\partial \mathbf{D}}{\partial t} + \mathbf{J}, \qquad \operatorname{div} \mathbf{D} = \rho.$$

$$\operatorname{curl} \mathbf{E} = -\frac{\partial \mathbf{B}}{\partial t}, \qquad \operatorname{div} \mathbf{B} = 0.$$

(9)

Equations (9) are, however, not the truly basic laws. They are derived mathematically from Maxwell's equations in integral form:

$$\int_{\partial A} H_t \, ds = \iint_A J_n \, d\sigma + \frac{d}{dt} \iint_A D_n \, d\sigma,$$

$$\int_{\partial A} E_t \, ds = -\frac{d}{dt} \iint_A B_n \, d\sigma, \tag{10}$$

where A is a stationary (i.e., not moving) surface region, with boundary ∂A. The second equation of (10) is also known as Faraday's induction law.

I must mention here that the equations div $\mathbf{D} = \rho$, div $\mathbf{B} = 0$, contain some information which is not derived from Eq. (10). I shall discuss this point later.

Let us rewrite Equations (10) in more suitable notation. First, I replace $H_t \, ds$ with $[\mathbf{H}]_1$, $J_n \, d\sigma$ with $[\mathbf{J}]_2$, and so on. Second, I integrate both equations over a time interval I, say from $t = a$ to $t = b$. With these changes, Equations (10) become:

$$\int_a^b dt \int_{\partial A} [\mathbf{H}]_1 = \int_a^b dt \iint_A [\mathbf{J}]_2 + \iint_A [\mathbf{D}]_2 \Big|_{t=a}^{t=b},$$

$$\int_a^b dt \int_{\partial A} [\mathbf{E}]_1 = - \iint_A [\mathbf{B}]_2 \Big|_{t=a}^{t=b}. \tag{11}$$

Equations (11) invite comparison with Equations (7) and (8). In order to exploit this comparison, I introduce three differential forms

$$\lambda = [\mathbf{B}]_2 - dt[\mathbf{E}]_1,$$

$$\kappa = [\mathbf{D}]_2 + dt[\mathbf{H}]_1, \tag{12}$$

$$\tau = \rho \, dx \, dy \, dz - dt[\mathbf{J}]_2.$$

Now the comparison of (11) with (7) and (8) shows that we have:

$$\int_{\partial(I \times A)} \kappa = \int_{I \times A} \tau, \qquad \int_{\partial(I \times A)} \lambda = 0. \tag{13}$$

Let us discuss these equations.

If you compare (12) with my table of electrodynamical fields, you will see immediately that the three differential forms λ, κ, τ in four-dimensional space represent the three fields of the table. But how did the term $\rho \, dx \, dy \, dz$ get into τ? It does not occur in Equations (11).

Let me try to explain this. In physics, electrical current is often described as a flow of electrical charges, with charge density ρ and flow velocity $\mathbf{J}$. Apart from nuclear reactions, and we do not consider these here, electrical charges are neither generated nor destroyed. This is expressed mathematically by the so-called continuity equation:

$$\operatorname{div} \mathbf{J} + \frac{\partial \rho}{\partial t} = 0 .$$

If you compare this with Equation (4), you see that the continuity equation becomes, in our notation,

$$d\tau = 0. \tag{14}$$

This is the reason for the term $\rho \, dx \, dy \, dz$ in τ.

Let us now discuss Equations (13). It seems natural to generalize these equations a little bit; we write:

$$\int_{\partial R} \kappa = \int_R \tau, \qquad \int_{\partial R} \lambda = 0, \tag{15}$$

where R now is any three-dimensional region in four-dimensional space, with time and the three-space coordinates as coordinates, with a well-behaved boundary ∂R. Equations (15) are the most general form of Maxwell's equations.

Just how much more do Equations (15) say than Equations (13)? And how are they related to Maxwell's equations in their familiar form (9)?

Before answering these questions, let me discuss what a three-dimensional region R in four-dimensional space means. Suppose you keep the time t fixed. If you do this, you obtain, in general, a two-dimensional cross section of the region R, and this you interpret as a region A of a surface in three-space. If you change t, this cross section will change, too. This has a rather obvious interpretation: the surface region A is moving. Thus Equations (15) are the generalization of Equations (10) and (13) from a stationary surface region to a moving surface region in three-space.

Now let us explore Equations (15). Using the generalized theorem of Stokes, Equation (6), we can rewrite (15) in the form

$$\int_R d\kappa = \int_R \tau, \qquad \int_R d\lambda = 0.$$

Since the region R is arbitrary, we conclude that

$$d\kappa = \tau, \qquad d\lambda = 0. \tag{16}$$

Now recall Equations (12) which define λ, κ, τ, and look at Equations (4). You will see that Equations (16) say exactly the same thing as Equations (9). In other words, Equations (16) are Maxwell's equations in differential form, expressed in terms of differential forms in four-dimensional space.

If we integrate Equations (16) over a three-dimensional region R and use Stokes's theorem, we obtain Equations (15). Thus it would seem that Equations (15) and (16) contain the same amount of information. Actually, this is not the case. Equations (9) and (16) are not valid on the boundary of two media, where discontinuities of the electromagnetic fields may occur. Equations (15), however, remain valid even if the region R straddles such a boundary, and thus they can be made to furnish full information about field discontinuities at boundaries. For the case of a stationary boundary, this information can be obtained from Equations (10) and (13); for a moving boundary, the general Equations (15) are needed. This is a very interesting topic, but I cannot pursue it here.

I have yet to discuss how much more Equations (15) say than Equations (10) and (13). Let me remark first that (14) is a consequence of (16). If we differentiate both sides of the first equation of (16) and use Equation (5), we obtain (14). Now let us look at (13). Using Stokes's theorem, we obtain:

$$\int_{I \times A} d\kappa = \int_{I \times A} \tau, \qquad \int_{I \times A} d\lambda = 0.$$

Because of Equation (8), we cannot conclude from this that $d\kappa = \tau$ or that $d\lambda = 0$. We can only conclude that

$$dt\left[\operatorname{curl} \mathbf{H} - \frac{\partial \mathbf{D}}{\partial t}\right]_2 = dt[\mathbf{J}]_2 \quad \text{and} \quad dt\left[\operatorname{curl} \mathbf{E} + \frac{\partial \mathbf{B}}{\partial t}\right]_2 = 0.$$

In other words, we obtain the equations on the left side of (9). Using (4) for κ and λ, and the equations just obtained, we have

$$\tau - d\kappa = (\rho - \operatorname{div} \mathbf{D}) \, dx \, dy \, dz,$$

$$d\lambda = (\operatorname{div} \mathbf{B}) \, dx \, dy \, dz.$$

If we differentiate these equations, using (5) and assuming (14), we obtain:

$$\frac{\partial}{\partial t} (\rho - \operatorname{div} \mathbf{D}) \, dt \, dx \, dy \, dz = 0; \qquad \frac{\partial}{\partial t} (\operatorname{div} \mathbf{B}) \, dt \, dx \, dy \, dz = 0.$$

In other words, the fields $\rho - \operatorname{div} \mathbf{D}$ and $\operatorname{div} \mathbf{B}$ are stationary, i.e., constant at any fixed point of space. Thus these fields vanish at all times if they vanish initially.

Now our questions are answered. If we replace Equations (10) and (13) by Equations (15), we make two additional assumptions. We assume that electrical charges are neither generated nor destroyed, and we assume that the stationary fields $\rho - \operatorname{div} \mathbf{D}$ and $\operatorname{div} \mathbf{B}$ vanish in the beginning, and hence always. There are ample physical reasons for making these assumptions.

4. FURTHER DISCUSSION

Equations (15) and (16) do not tell the whole story. The two electromagnetic fields are connected, but their connection depends on the medium in which they act. In a homogeneous, isotropic medium, the connection is given by

$$\mathbf{D} = \varepsilon\mathbf{E}, \qquad \mathbf{B} = \mu\mathbf{H}, \qquad \text{with} \qquad \varepsilon\mu = \frac{1}{c^2}, \tag{17}$$

where ε and μ are permittivity and permeability of the medium, and c is the speed of light.

Before we can "translate" (17) into equations for κ and λ, we need some additional techniques of exterior differential calculus.

The *star operator* is defined in three-space as follows:

$$\begin{aligned}
*f &= f\,dx\,dy\,dz, & *(f\,dx\,dy\,dz) &= f, \\
*[\mathbf{U}]_1 &= [\mathbf{U}]_2, & *[\mathbf{U}]_2 &= [\mathbf{U}]_1
\end{aligned} \tag{18}$$

We note that the star operator is linear and satisfies

$$*(*\omega) = \omega \tag{19}$$

for any differential form ω in three-space.

In space-time, the four-dimensional space of physics, we put

$$*f = cf\,dt\,dx\,dy\,dz,$$

$$*([\mathbf{U}]_1 - f\,dt) = c\,dt[\mathbf{U}]_2 - \frac{1}{c}f\,dx\,dy\,dz,$$

$$*([\mathbf{P}]_2 - dt[\mathbf{U}]_1) = \frac{1}{c}[\mathbf{U}]_2 + c\,dt[\mathbf{P}]_1, \tag{20}$$

$$*(f\,dx\,dy\,dz - dt[\mathbf{P}]_2) = cf\,dt - \frac{1}{c}[\mathbf{P}]_1,$$

$$*(f\,dt\,dx\,dy\,dz) = -\frac{1}{c}f.$$

The star operator is linear, and we have

$$*(*\omega) = (-1)^{r-1}\omega \tag{21}$$

for a differential form ω of order r in space-time.

In a space with a star operator on differential forms, the *codifferential* $\delta\omega$ of a differential form ω of positive order r is defined by

$$*(\delta\omega) = (-1)^{r-1} d(*\omega), \tag{22}$$

and the *generalized Laplace operator* Δ on differential forms is defined by

$$\Delta f = \delta(df) \tag{23}$$

for a scalar field f, and by

$$\Delta\omega = d(\delta\omega) + \delta(d\omega) \tag{24}$$

for a differential form ω of positive order.

The operators δ and Δ obviously are linear. In three-space and in space-time, the operator Δ turns out to be a scalar operator, i.e.

$$\Delta(f\xi) = (\Delta f)\xi$$

if f is a scalar field and ξ a product of coordinate differentials. In three-space, Δ is the ordinary Laplace operator. In space-time, we have

$$\Delta f = \frac{1}{c^2}\frac{\partial^2 f}{\partial t^2} - \frac{\partial^2 f}{\partial x^2} - \frac{\partial^2 f}{\partial y^2} - \frac{\partial^2 f}{\partial z^2}\ .$$

In other words, Δ is the operator of the wave equation.

You may find a full treatment of the star operator, and of the operators δ and Δ, in the book by Flanders which I quoted earlier in this lecture, but I must warn you that his treatment differs from mine. In particular, he and I use opposite signs in the definition of δ, and hence also in Δ. His treatment is better for geometry; my treatment seems to be preferable for physics. Thus there are good arguments on both sides, but I cannot discuss this here.

If we apply (20) to (12) and use (17), we obtain

$$*\lambda = \frac{1}{c}\,[\mathbf{E}]_2 + c\,dt[\mathbf{B}]_I = \frac{1}{c\varepsilon}\,\kappa = (c\mu)\kappa,$$

$$(25)$$

$$*\tau = c\rho\,dt - \frac{1}{c}\,[\mathbf{J}]_1.$$

If we use this with (21) and (22), Equations (16) become

$$\delta\lambda = -\frac{1}{c\varepsilon}\,(*\tau) = -(c\mu)(*\tau), \qquad d\lambda = 0. \qquad (26)$$

These are Maxwell's equations for a homogeneous, isotropic medium.

By a theorem of exterior differential calculus, it follows from $d\lambda = 0$ that there is a differential form α of order 1 such that

$$d\alpha = \lambda, \qquad \delta\alpha = 0. \qquad (27)$$

Because of (26), this form α satisfies the wave equation:

$$\Delta\alpha = -\frac{1}{c\varepsilon}\,(*\tau) = -(c\mu)(*\tau). \qquad (28)$$

The differential form α is called the *electromagnetic potential*.

If we put $\alpha = [\mathbf{A}]_1 - \varphi\,dt$, then φ is the *scalar potential* and $\mathbf{A}$ the *vector potential* of the electromagnetic field $\lambda = [\mathbf{B}]_2 - dt[\mathbf{E}]_1$, and Equations (27) become

$$\operatorname{curl}\mathbf{A} = \mathbf{B}, \qquad \operatorname{grad}\varphi + \frac{\partial A}{\partial t} = -\mathbf{E},$$

$$\frac{1}{c^2}\frac{\partial\varphi}{\partial t} + \operatorname{div}\mathbf{A} = 0.$$

The last of these equations is called the Lorentz condition for the electromagnetic potential.

I hope that my lecture has shown to you that exterior differential calculus is a very useful tool for the physicist and the engineer as well as for the mathematician. If you want to learn more about this tool, so that you will be able to use it, my goal has been achieved.

5. APPENDIX: ELECTROMAGNETIC UNITS

Electrodynamics have been plagued by a host of systems of units. What is worse, changing units means changing the appearance of the basic laws such as Maxwell's equations. There is, however, a simple way of coping with these difficulties which I have learned from Professor F. Gassmann of the Swiss Federal Institute of Technology and which may be profitable to readers of my lecture.

One defines *system factors* $\hat{c}$ and $\hat{p}$ as follows. $\hat{c} = 1$ in the electrostatic, magnetostatic, and mksa systems, and $\hat{c} = c$ (speed of light, in cm/sec) in the Gaussian system. $\hat{p} = 1$ in "rationalized" systems (with a factor $1/4\pi$ in Coulomb's law), and $\hat{p} = 4\pi$ in "classical" systems (without this factor).

Permittivity ε_0 and permeability μ_0 of the vacuum may also be regarded as system factors. $\varepsilon_0 = 1$ in the electrostatic and Gaussian systems, $\mu_0 = 1$ in the magnetostatic and Gaussian systems, and

$$\mu_0 = \frac{4\pi}{\hat{p}} \, 10^{-7} \text{ volt sec/amp m}$$

in the mksa system. $\varepsilon_0 \mu_0 = (\hat{c}/c)^2$ in any system.

In my lecture, I have used the rationalized mksa system or Giorgi system. In order to "translate" the formulas of the lecture into any other system of units, one may leave **B** and **D** unchanged, replace **E** and **H** by $\hat{c}\mathbf{E}$ and $\hat{c}\mathbf{H}$, replace ρ and **J** by $\hat{p}\rho$ and $\hat{p}\mathbf{J}$, and replace ε and μ by $\varepsilon/\hat{c}$ and $\mu/\hat{c}$.

9

Continuous Square Roots

of Mappings

M. K. FORT, JR.

The late M. K. Fort, Jr., Barrow Professor of Mathematics at the University of Georgia at the time of his death in 1964, was born in Spartanburg, South Carolina in 1921. After graduating from Wofford College he earned his Ph.D. at the University of Virginia in 1948. He taught at the Universities of Illinois, Mississippi, Virginia, and Georgia, where he became chairman of the department in 1959. He was a Ford Foundation Faculty Fellow in 1952–1953 and an Alfred P. Sloan Research Fellow in 1958–1961. His major interests and publications were in topology. Before his untimely death he agreed to publish this paper based on one of his most popular lectures, but since he was unable to see it through the press, any oversights and errors must be attributed to the Editor.

Although Professor Fort's lecture deals with functions of a complex variable, it presupposes only a familiarity with elementary properties of complex numbers and some theorems on continuity usually proved in advanced calculus courses.

CONTINUOUS SQUARE ROOTS OF MAPPINGS

M. K. Fort, Jr.

We are going to prove some theorems about continuous functions whose domains and ranges are sets of complex numbers. For brevity, a continuous function is usually called a *mapping*. We let C_0 denote the set of all non-zero complex numbers.

If f and φ are complex valued functions which have the same domain, φ is a *continuous square root* of f if: (i) φ is a mapping (i.e., φ is continuous), and (ii) $\varphi(z)^2 = f(z)$ for all z (i.e., φ is a square root of f). The notion of continuous square roots of mappings can be used to tell whether or not a subset of the plane has a "hole" in it.

To be more precise, if A is a bounded closed subset of the plane, then there are no holes in A if and only if every mapping of A into C_0 has a continuous square root.

If A is any one of the sets in Figure 9-1, then each mapping of A into C_0 has a continuous square root. (Theorem 1 proves this for the case of the disk.) If A is any one of the sets in Figure 9-2, then there exists a mapping of A into C_0 which does not have a continuous square root. (In case A is the circle, this result follows easily from Theorem 2.)

Theorem 3 is extremely useful in proving that certain functions have zeros. We apply it to obtain several "pay off" theorems, including the Fundamental Theorem of Algebra and the Brouwer Fixed Point Theorem for Disks.

169

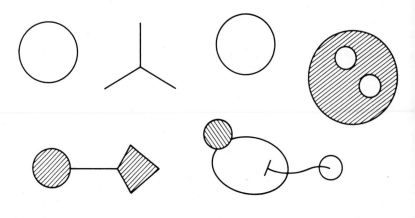

Fig. 9-1   Fig. 9-2

We begin by proving two lemmas which are needed for Theorem 1. We assume the reader is familiar with the elementary properties of the complex plane, and knows those theorems about continuous functions which are usually proved in advanced calculus courses. If A is a subset of the domain of a function f, $f\,|\,A$ denotes the function g whose domain is A and which satisfies $g(x) = f(x)$ for all $x \in A$.

Lemma 1. *If* $G = \{x + iy \,|\, x^2 + y^2 = 1 \ \text{and} \ x > -1\}$, *then the identity mapping on G has a continuous square root.*

PROOF: We define $\Phi(x + iy) = (x + 1 + iy)/\sqrt{2x + 2}$ for all $x + iy \in G$. Φ is obviously continuous on G, and computation shows that

$$\Phi(x + iy)^2 = \frac{x^2 + 2x + 1 - y^2 + 2(x + 1)yi}{2(x + 1)}$$

$$= \frac{2x^2 + 2x + 2(x + 1)yi}{2(x + 1)}$$

$$= x + yi.$$

The proof is complete, but in order to make the function Φ seem a little less mysterious we remark that if α is the angle (between π and $-\pi$) from the positive x axis to the half line from 0 through $x + iy$, then $\alpha/2$ is the angle from the positive x axis to the half line from 0 through $\Phi(x + iy)$.

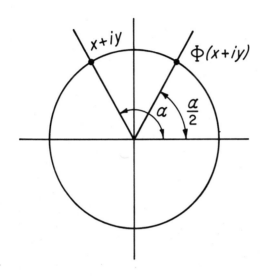

FIG. 9-3

G is the set of all points on the unit circle S^1 except -1. The fact that G does not include -1 is quite essential, since we will show later in Theorem 2 that the identity mapping on S^1 does not have a continuous square root.

Lemma 2. *If f and g are mappings such that*: (i) *f and g have the same domain X,* (ii) *the ranges of f and g are contained in the unit circle S^1, and* (iii) *$f(t) + g(t) \neq 0$ for all $t \in X$, then f has a continuous square root if and only if g does.*

PROOF: We first show that f/g has a continuous square root (regardless of whether or not f and g have continuous square roots). It follows from (iii) that $f(t)/g(t) \neq -1$ for all $t \in X$. Since the quotient of two members of the unit circle S^1 is a member of S^1, we see that $f(t)/g(t) \in G$ for all $t \in X$, where G is the set defined in Lemma 1. Letting Φ be the mapping obtained in Lemma 1, we define

$$h(t) = \Phi(f(t)/(g(t))$$

for all $t \in X$. Clearly h is a continuous square root of f/g.

We complete the proof of Lemma 2 by observing that if φ is a continuous square root of f, then φ/h is a continuous square root of $f/(f/g) = g$, and if ψ is a continuous square root of g, then $\psi \cdot h$ is a continuous square root of $g \cdot (f/g) = f$.

Lemma 3. If f is a mapping whose domain is a circle S and whose range is contained in a finite set F of complex numbers, then f is a constant mapping.

PROOF: Since F is finite, there exists $\varepsilon > 0$ such that if u and v are members of F and $u \neq v$ then $|u - v| > \varepsilon$. Since S is a bounded closed set, f is uniformly continuous on S. Therefore there exists $\delta > 0$ such that if z and w are members of S and $|z - w| < \delta$, then $|f(z) - f(w)| < \varepsilon$. It follows that if z and w are members of S and $|z - w| < \delta$, then $f(z) = f(w)$.

Now let s and t be any two members of S. There are points $z_0, z_1, \ldots, z_n$ on S such that $z_0 = s$, $z_n = t$ and $|z_{j+1} - z_j| < \delta$ for $0 \leqslant j < n$. It follows that $f(z_{j+1}) = f(z_j)$ for $0 \leqslant j < n$, and hence $f(s) = f(t)$. This proves that f is constant.

Theorem 1. If f is a mapping whose domain is a closed disk D having center at 0 and whose range is contained in C_0, then f has a continuous square root.

PROOF: We first define $g(z) = |f(z)|$ and $h(z) = f(z)/|f(z)|$ for all $z \in D$. Both g and h are mappings and $f = g \cdot h$. Since g is positive valued, we can define a continuous square root of g by letting

$\psi(z) = \sqrt{g(z)}$ for all $z \in D$. It follows that f has a continuous square root if h does. We now prove that h has a continuous square root.

Since D is a bounded closed set and h is continuous on D, h is uniformly continuous on D. Thus, there exists $\delta > 0$ such that if u and v are in D and $|u - v| < \delta$, then $|h(u) - h(v)| < 1$. We let r be the radius of D and choose a positive integer n such that $r/n < \delta$.

Now, if $z \in D$ and j is an integer such that $0 \leqslant j \leqslant n$, we define

$$h_j(z) = h(jz/n).$$

Since $|h(z)| = 1$ for all $z \in D$, each of the functions $h_0, h_1, \ldots, h_n$ is a mapping of D into the unit circle S^1.

Suppose

$$0 \leqslant j < n \qquad \text{and} \qquad z \in D.$$

Since

$$\left| \frac{(j+1)z}{n} - \frac{jz}{n} \right| = \left| \frac{z}{n} \right| \leqslant \frac{r}{n} < \delta,$$

we obtain

$$|h_{j+1}(z) - h_j(z)| = \left| h\left(\frac{(j+1)z}{n} \right) - h\left(\frac{jz}{n} \right) \right| < 1.$$

Since $h_{j+1}(z)$ and $h_j(z)$ are both on the unit circle, this implies $h_{j+1}(z) + h_j(z) \neq 0$. It follows from Lemma 2 that for each j, h_j has a continuous square root if and only if h_{j+1} has a continuous square root.

Since $h_0(z) = h(0)$ for all $z \in D$, h_0 is a constant mapping, and hence h_0 obviously has a continuous square root. We now see that h_j has a continuous square root for each j, $0 \leqslant j \leqslant n$. However, $h = h_n$ and so h has a continuous square root. This completes the proof of Theorem 1.

Theorem 2.   If f is a mapping whose domain is a circle S with center 0, whose range is contained in C_0, and which satisfies

$$f(-z) = -f(z)$$

for all $z \in S$, then f does not have a continuous square root.

PROOF: We shall give a proof by contradiction. Thus, we assume that f has a continuous square root φ. For each $z \in S$, we define

$$g(z) = \frac{\varphi(-z)}{\varphi(z)}.$$

g is a mapping, and

$$g(z)^2 = \frac{\varphi(-z)^2}{\varphi(z)^2} = \frac{f(-z)}{f(z)} = \frac{-f(z)}{f(z)} = -1$$

for all $z \in S$. Thus g is a mapping whose range is contained in the finite set $\{i, -i\}$. By Lemma 3, g is a constant function. Therefore there is a complex number k, $k = i$ or $k = -i$, such that $g(z) = k$ for all $z \in S$. It follows that if $z \in S$,

$$-1 = k \cdot k = g(z) \cdot g(-z) = \frac{\varphi(-z)}{\varphi(z)} \cdot \frac{\varphi(z)}{\varphi(-z)} = 1.$$

This is a contradiction. Hence f does not have a continuous square root.

Lemma 4.   If f is a mapping whose domain is a circle S and whose range is contained in C_0, then f has at most two continuous square roots.

PROOF: It is obviously sufficient to prove that if φ and ψ are any two continuous square roots of f, then either $\varphi = \psi$ or $\varphi = -\psi$.

Let us assume that φ and ψ are continuous square roots of f. We define

$$g(z) = \frac{\varphi(z)}{\psi(z)}$$

for all $z \in S$. g is a mapping, and

$$g(z)^2 = \frac{\varphi(z)^2}{\psi(z)^2} = \frac{f(z)}{f(z)} = 1$$

for all $z \in S$. Thus the range of g is contained in the finite set $\{1, -1\}$. It follows from Lemma 3 that g is constant. Thus $g(z) = 1$ for all $z \in S$ or $g(z) = -1$ for all $z \in S$. This implies that either $\varphi = \psi$ or $\varphi = -\psi$.

Theorem 3. *Let D be a closed disk with center at 0 and let S be the boundary of D. If f is a mapping of D into the complex plane such that either*

(A) $f(-z) = -f(z)$ *for all $z \in S$, or*
(B) *there is an integer $n \neq 0$ such that $f(z) = z^n$ for all $z \in S$,*

then there exists $q \in D$ such that $f(q) = 0$.

PROOF: We shall consider three cases.

CASE 1: f satisfies hypothesis (A).

Let us assume $f(z) \neq 0$ for all $z \in D$. Then, by Theorem 1, f has a continuous square root φ. It follows that $\varphi \,|\, S$ is a continuous square root of $f \,|\, S$. Theorem 2, however, states that $f \,|\, S$ does not have a continuous square root. We have a contradiction. Hence there exists $q \in D$ such that $f(q) = 0$.

CASE 2: f satisfies hypothesis (B) for some $n > 0$.

We prove this case by induction on n, making use of Case 1 which has already been established.

If $n = 1$, then for all $z \in S$,

$$f(-z) = (-z)^1 = -(z^1) = -f(z).$$

Thus f satisfies (A) and by Case 1 we know that $f(z) = 0$ for some $q \in D$.

We now assume $n > 1$, and assume the theorem true for all positive integers k such that $k < n$. If n is odd, f satisfies (A) and by Case 1 there exists $q \in D$ such that $f(q) = 0$. Let us consider the case n even, so that $n = 2m$ for some positive integer m.

Suppose $f(z) \neq 0$ for all $z \in D$. Then, by Theorem 1, f has a continuous square root φ. We define $\alpha(z) = z^m$ and $\beta(z) = -z^m$ for all $z \in S$. Since $g(z) = z^n = (z^m)^2$ for all $z \in S$, the mappings α, β and $\varphi \mid S$ are all continuous square roots of $f \mid S$. Clearly $\alpha \neq \beta$, and so by Lemma 4 either $\varphi \mid S = \alpha$ or $\varphi \mid S = \beta$. Since φ and $-\varphi$ are both continuous square roots of f, we may assume without loss of generality that φ has been chosen so that $\varphi \mid S = \alpha$. Since $m < n$ and φ is a mapping of D into the complex plane such that $\varphi(z) = z^m$ for all $z \in S$, by our inductive hypothesis there exists $q \in D$ such that $\varphi(q) = 0$. This implies $f(q) = \varphi(q)^2 = 0^2 = 0$, which contradicts the assumption that $f(z) \neq 0$ for all $z \in D$. Accordingly, there exists $q \in D$ such that $f(q) = 0$.

CASE 3: f satisfies hypothesis (B) for some $n < 0$.

Let us assume $f(z) \neq 0$ for all $z \in D$. We define $g(z) = 1/f(z)$ for all $z \in D$. The mapping g satisfies the hypothesis for Case 2, and so there exists $q \in D$ such that $g(q) = 0$. This is impossible since $g(q) = 1/f(q) \neq 0$. Hence, there exists $q \in D$ such that $f(q) = 0$.

Theorem 4.   (The Fundamental Theorem of Algebra). *If*
$$P(z) = a_0 z^n + a_1 z^{n-1} + \cdots + a_n$$
for all complex numbers z, n a positive integer and $a_0 \neq 0$, then there exists q such that $P(q) = 0$.

PROOF: We assume $a_0 = 1$, since there is no loss of generality in doing this.

We define
$$r = 1 + |a_1| + |a_2| + \cdots + |a_n|$$
and observe that if $|z| > r$, then
$$\begin{aligned}
|P(z) - z^n| &= |a_1 z^{n-1} + a_2 z^{n-2} + \cdots + a_n| \\
&\leqslant |a_1| \cdot |z^{n-1}| + |a_2| \cdot |z^{n-2}| + \cdots + |a_n| \\
&\leqslant |a_1| \cdot |z^{n-1}| + |a_2| \cdot |z^{n-1}| + \cdots + |a_n| \cdot |z^{n-1}| \\
&= |z^{n-1}| \cdot (|a_1| + |a_2| + \cdots + |a_n|) \\
&< |z^{n-1}| \cdot r \\
&< |z^n|.
\end{aligned}$$

The inequality $|P(z) - z^n| < |z^n|$ states that the distance from z^n to 0 is greater than the distance from z^n to $P(z)$, and this implies that 0 is not on the line segment joining z^n to $P(z)$. Recall that if a and b are real numbers such that $a \geqslant 0$, $b \geqslant 0$, and $a + b = 1$, then $a \cdot z^n + b \cdot P(z)$ *is* on the segment from z^n to $P(z)$. We now know that if $|z| \geqslant r$, $a \geqslant 0$, $b \geqslant 0$, and $a + b = 1$, then $a \cdot z^n + b \cdot P(z) \neq 0$.

Let $A = \{z \mid r \leqslant |z| \leqslant 2r\}$. For each $z \in A$ we define:

$$a(z) = \frac{|z|}{r} - 1,$$

$$b(z) = 2 - \frac{|z|}{r},$$

and

$$g(z) = a(z) \cdot z^n + b(z) \cdot P(z).$$

Clearly g is continuous on A, and $g(z) = P(z)$ if $|z| = r$. Moreover, since $a(z) \geqslant 0$, $b(z) \geqslant 0$, and $a(z) + b(z) = 1$ for all $z \in A$, $g(z) \neq 0$ for all $z \in A$.

We now let $B = \{z \mid |z| \leqslant r\}$ and $D = \{z \mid |z| \leqslant 2r\}$. For $z \in D$, we define

$$f(z) = \begin{cases} g(z) \text{ if } z \in A \\ P(z) \text{ if } z \in B. \end{cases}$$

The function f is well defined since $g(z) = P(z)$ if z is in both A and B. Since g is continuous on A, P is continuous on B, and A and B are closed subsets of D, it follows that f is continuous on D.

If $|z| = 2r$, then $a(z) = 1$, $b(z) = 0$ and $f(z) = g(z) = z^n$. Thus f satisfies the hypothesis of Theorem 3 and there exists $q \in D$ such that $f(q) = 0$. We know $q \notin A$, since $g(z) \neq 0$ for all $z \in A$. Hence $q \in B$ and $f(q) = P(q)$. Thus $P(q) = 0$, and we have proved the theorem.

If A and B are subsets of the plane (or of any topological space) and $A \subset B$, then A is a *retract* of B if and only if there exists a mapping f having domain B and range A such that $f(z) = z$ for all $z \in A$. As an example, note that if A in Figure 9-4

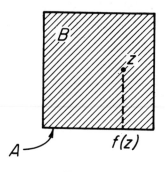

FIG. 9-4

is a side of a solid square B, then A is a retract of B since we can project B onto A keeping points of A fixed. In topology it is often important to know whether or not one set is a retract of another.

Theorem 5. If S is the boundary of a closed disk D, then S is not a retract of D.

PROOF: There is no loss of generality in choosing our coordinates so that the center of D is at 0. Let us assume that S is a retract of D. Then there is a mapping f with domain D and range S such that $f(z) = z$ for $z \in S$. Since f satisfies the hypothesis of Theorem 3, there exists $q \in D$ such that $f(q) = 0$. This is impossible since $0 \notin S$. Hence S is not a retract of D.

The Intermediate Value Theorem of calculus can be used to prove that the boundary of a closed interval is not a retract of the interval. The reader is urged to work out the details of the proof of this one-dimensional analogue of Theorem 5. Higher-dimensional versions of Theorem 5 also exist, but they are much harder to prove.

A point p is a *fixed point* of a mapping f if p is in the domain of f and $f(p) = p$. Our final theorem is one of the best known theorems of topology.

Theorem 6.   (Brouwer Fixed Point Theorem for Disks.) *If f is a mapping whose domain is a closed disk D and whose range is contained in D, then f has a fixed point.*

PROOF: Assume $f(z) \neq z$ for all $z \in D$. We are going to show that in this case there exists a mapping g whose domain is D, whose range is the boundary S of D, and which satisfies $g(z) = z$ for all $z \in D$. The existence of such a mapping g implies that S is a retract of D, and this contradicts Theorem 5. Hence we see that there must exist $q \in D$ such that $f(q) = q$, and f has a fixed point.

Geometrically, g is quite easy to describe. (See Figure 9-5.) We let $L(z)$ be the ray (half line) which starts at $f(z)$ and passes through z. $L(z)$ intersects the circle S in a unique point which we define to be $g(z)$.

For the sake of rigor, we now give a non-geometric description of the mapping g. Unfortunately, this second description is considerably longer than the first and is also less intuitive.

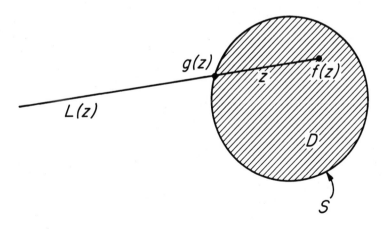

FIG. 9-5

We assume that the center of D is at 0 and that the radius of D is 1, since there is no loss of generality in doing this.

For each real number s, we define

$$F(z, s) = |s \cdot [z - f(z)] + f(z)|^2 - 1.$$

We can write

$$F(z, s) = a(z) \cdot s^2 + b(z) \cdot s + c(z),$$

where a, b, and c are real valued and continuous functions. Since $a(z) = |z - f(z)|^2 > 0$ and $c(z) = |f(z)|^2 - 1 \leqslant 0$, for each z the equation

$$\text{(E)} \quad a(z) \cdot s^2 + b(z) \cdot s + c(z) = 0$$

has real roots, at most one of which is positive. We define a mapping r by

$$r(z) = \frac{-b(z) + \sqrt{b(z)^2 - 4a(z)c(z)}}{2a(z)}.$$

If $|z| = 1$, then 1 is a root of (E) since $F(z, 1) = |z|^2 - 1 = 0$. Since $r(z)$ is the largest root of (E) and (E) has at most one positive root, it follows that $r(z) = 1$ if $|z| = 1$.

We define

$$g(z) = r(z) \cdot [z - f(z)] + f(z)$$

for all $z \in D$.

Since $|g(z)|^2 - 1 = F[z, r(z)] = 0$ for all z, $|g(z)| = 1$. Thus g is a mapping of D into the boundary of D. If $|z| = 1$, then $r(z) = 1$ and $g(z) = z$. Hence the mapping g retracts D onto the boundary of D, contradicting Theorem 5. Since the existence of g was implied by the assumption that $f(z) \neq z$ for all $z \in D$, it follows that there must exist a point p in D such that $f(p) = p$.